J. WESTON
WALCH
PUBLISHER
Portland, Maine

EASY
Science Demos & Labs

MW00388068

Earth Science

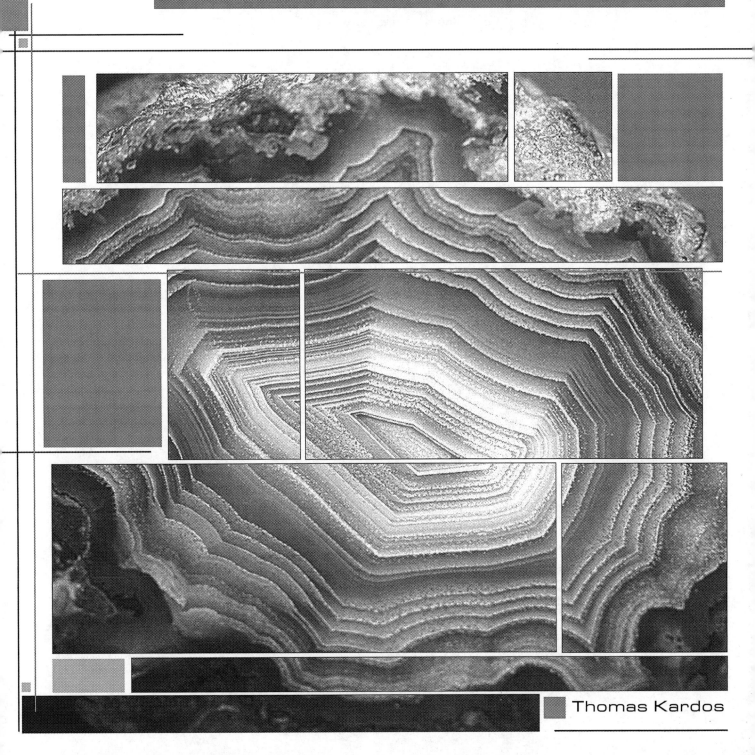

Thomas Kardos

User's Guide
to
Walch Reproducible Books

Dedication

This book is dedicated to my darling wife, Pearl, who throughout this project assisted me with great patience. As a nonscience educator, she helped me develop this book into an easy-to-use and comprehensible resource.

Cover photo: agate

1   2   3   4   5   6   7   8   9   10
ISBN 0-8251-4500-7
Copyright © 1997, 2003
J. Weston Walch, Publisher
P.O. Box 658 • Portland, Maine 04104-0658
walch.com
Printed in the United States of America

Contents

Demos and Labs

Appendix

Preface

As a middle school teacher, many times I found myself wishing for a quick and easy demonstration to illustrate a word, a concept, or a principle in science. Also, I often wanted a brief explanation to conveniently review basics and additional information without going to several texts.

This book is a collection of many classroom demonstrations. Explanation is provided so that you can quickly review key concepts. Basic science ideas are hard to present on a concrete level; the demonstrations fill that specific need. You will also find 10 specially created laboratory activities for middle school students that are safe enough for young people to do on their own. These labs add a deeper level of understanding to the demonstrations.

An actual teacher demonstration is something full of joy and expectation, like a thriller with a twist ending. Keep it that way and enjoy it! Try everything beforehand.

We need to support each other and leave footprints in the sands of time. Teaching is a living art. Happy journey! Happy sciencing!

—*Thomas Kardos*

National Science Education Standards for Middle School

The goals for school science that underlie the National Science Education Standards are to educate students who are able to

- experience the richness and excitement of knowing about and understanding the natural world;

- use appropriate scientific processes and principles in making personal decisions;

- engage intelligently in public discourse and debate about matters of scientific and technological concern; and

- increase their economic productivity through the use of the knowledge, understanding, and skills of the scientifically literate person in their careers.

These abilities define a scientifically literate society. The standards for content define what the scientifically literate person should know, understand, and be able to do after 13 years of school science. Laboratory science is an important part of high school science, and to that end we have included student labs in this series.

Between grades 5 and 8, students move away from simple observation of the natural world and toward inquiry-based methodology. Mathematics in science becomes an important tool. Below are the major topics students will explore in each subject.

- Earth and Space Science: Structure of the earth system, earth's history, and earth in the solar system

- Biology: Structure and function in living systems, reproduction and heredity, regulation and behavior, populations and ecosystems, and diversity and adaptations of organisms

- Chemistry and Physics: Properties and changes of properties in matter, motions and forces, and transfer of energy

Our series, *Easy Science Demos and Labs*, addresses not only the national standards, but also the underlying concepts that must be understood before the national standards issues can be fully explored. By observing demonstrations and attempting laboratory exercises on their own, students can more fully understand the process of an inquiry-based system. Cross-curricular instruction, especially in mathematics, is possible for many of these labs and demonstrations.

Suggestions for Teachers

1. A • (bullet) denotes a demonstration. Several headings have multiple demonstrations.

2. **Materials:** Provides an accurate list of materials needed. You can make substitutions and changes as you find appropriate.

3. Since many demonstrations will not be clearly visible from the back of the room, you will need to take this into account as part of your classroom management technique. Students need to see the entire procedure, step by step.

4. Some demonstrations require that students make observations over a short period of time. It is important that students observe the changes in progress. One choice is to videotape the event and replay it several times.

5. Some demonstrations can be enhanced by bottom illumination: Place the demonstration on an overhead projector and lower the mirror so that no image is projected overhead.

6. I use a 30-cup coffeepot in lieu of an electric hot plate, pans, and more cumbersome equipment to heat water for student experiments and to perform many demonstrations.

7. As the metric system is the proper unit of measurement in a science class, metric units are used throughout this book. Where practical, we also provide the U.S. conventional equivalent.

8. Just a few demonstrations may appear difficult to set up, for they have many parts. Be patient, follow the listing's steps, and you will really succeed with them.

Equipment

- Sometimes, though rarely, I will call for equipment that you may not have. An increasing growth in technology tends to complicate matters. Skip these few demonstrations or borrow the equipment from your local high school teacher. Review with him or her the proper and safe use of it. These special demonstrations will add immensely to your power as an effective educator and will enhance your professionalism.

- Try all demonstrations in advance to smooth your show. If something fails, enjoy it and teach with it. Many great scientific discoveries had to be done over many times before their first success. Edwin Land had to do more than 11,000 experiments to develop the instant color photograph. Most people would have quit long before that.

- One of my favorite techniques is to record with a camcorder and show the demonstration on a large monitor.

Safety Procedures

- Follow all local, state, and federal safety procedures. Protect your students and yourself from harm.

- Attend safety classes to be up-to-date on the latest in classroom safety procedures. Much new legislation has been adopted in the recent past.

- Have evacuation plans clearly posted, planned, and actually tested.

- Conduct experiments involving chemicals only in rooms that are properly ventilated.

- Have an ABC-rated fire extinguisher on hand at all times. Use a Halon™ gas extinguisher for electronic equipment.

- Learn how to use a fire extinguisher properly.

- Label all containers and use original containers. Dispose of chemicals that are outdated.

- Know and teach an adequate method for disposing of broken glass.

- Heat sources, such as Bunsen burners and candles, can be hazardous. Use caution when heating chemicals.

- Wear required safety equipment at all times, including goggles, gloves, and smocks or labcoats.

- Never eat or drink in the laboratory.

- Practice your demonstration if it is totally new to you. A few demonstrations do require some prior practice.

- Conduct demonstrations at a distance so that no one is harmed should anything go wrong.

- Have students wash their hands whenever they come into contact with anything that may be remotely harmful to them, even if years later, like lead.

- Neutralize all acids and bases prior to disposal, if possible, in a chemical fume hood.

- Dispose of demonstration materials in a safe way. Obtain your district's guidelines on this matter.

- Be especially aware of the need to dispose of hazardous materials safely. Some chemistry experiments create byproducts that are harmful to the environment.

- Take appropriate precautions when working with electricity. Make sure hands are dry and clean, and never touch live wires, even if connected only to a battery. Never test a battery by mouth.

- When using lasers, never look directly into the beam, and make sure students understand the dangers of laser light.

Disclaimer: The safety rules are provided only as a guide. They are neither complete nor totally inclusive. The publisher and the author do not assume any responsibility for actions or consequences in following instructions provided in this book.

Demos and Labs

If one looked at the earth in cross section, one would observe the **crust,** the **mantle,** the **outer core,** and the **inner core.**

Materials: hard-boiled egg, knife

- Cut a hard-boiled egg and show the students the cross section. The egg has three layers: the shell, the white, and the yolk. Similarly, a cross section of the earth would reveal that it is structured in layers.

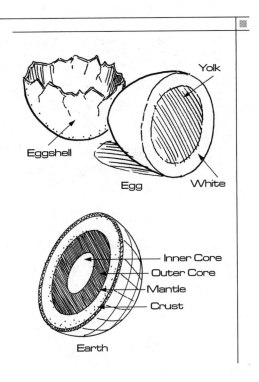

When geologists need information about the earth's structure, they drill for core samples.

Materials: straw, cupcake with filling and icing, razor blade, camcorder and monitor (optional)

- Gently insert the straw down through the middle of the cupcake. Remove the straw and carefully cut it open to observe the "core sample" of icing, cake, and filling. Use a camcorder, if available, to show a close-up of the entire demonstration.

Special Safety Consideration: Use extreme caution using razor blades in the classroom.

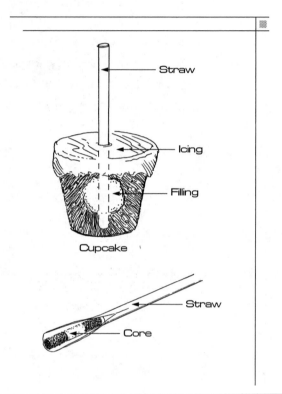

Straw

Icing

Filling

Cupcake

Straw

Core

The hardness test is critical in determining the properties of minerals. Follow the instructions of your hardness test kit. Use the close-up features of a camcorder, if one is available. The hardness scale is provided for your convenience.

TABLE: MOHS HARDNESS SCALE

Hardness Scale 1-10 Sample Materials	Test for Hardness
1. Talcum	Softest of materials; can be scratched by anything, even fingernail
2. Gypsum	Can be scratched by anything except talcum
3. Calcite	Can be scratched by a copper wire or penny
4. Fluorite	Can be scratched by a steel tool, knife, or nail file, but not easily
5. Apatite	Can be scratched by a steel tool or a nail file, but not easily
6. **Feldspar**	Can scratch glass and cannot be scratched by a knife
7. Quartz	Can scratch steel and glass
8. Topaz	Can scratch quartz
9. Corundum	Can scratch topaz
10. Diamond	Can scratch everything else

There is also a hardness scale 1–15. The diamond is also the hardest mineral on that scale.

Materials: hardness testing kit, sample minerals and materials, camcorder and monitor (optional), diamond-tipped glass cutter, small pieces of glass

- Test the hardness of several rocks, minerals, and other materials, using the hardness test kit.

- Scratch several lines on a piece of glass with the diamond-tipped cutter.

Long ago, coins made of gold or silver were tested in ancient marketplaces by rubbing them on the surface of a **touchstone,** a black siliceous stone related to flint. The streak that was left when precious metals were rubbed on the stone told the merchant whether the coin being used by a customer was genuine.

We still occasionally use a streak test for minerals. It is one way that minerals can be identified.

Materials: several minerals (whatever minerals you may have), ceramic tile (preferably with light-colored back)

- **Streaking** is an excellent test for identifying minerals. When you write on your chalkboard, you are streaking your chalk, or calcite, on the chalkboard surface. Minerals leave a characteristic powdery trail, called a streak. Some minerals seem to have several colors, but when you streak them, they leave a uniform color. Using several minerals, demonstrate streaking on the porous back of a ceramic tile.

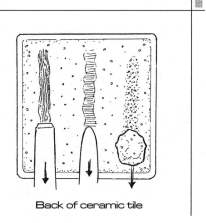

Back of ceramic tile

Minerals that contain iron and cobalt have magnetic properties.

Materials: magnet, minerals, compass

- Test the minerals with the magnet to see if they are attracted by it. **Lodestone** or other minerals containing large percentages of iron will be attracted, as will some meteorites.

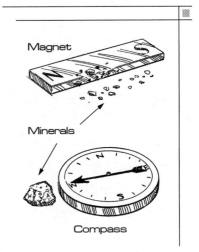

- Place the compass near the mineral to be tested to see if the needle moves. If it does, the material is magnetic.

Special Safety Consideration: This experiment uses ferrous material, since cobalt is a heavy metal.

Calcite is a soft, usually clear or white mineral. It is a base, and it reacts with acids by fizzing.

Materials: calcite mineral, weak hydrochloric acid (.5M solution), eyedropper

- Place several drops of weak hydrochloric acid on a rock suspected of being calcite. If it fizzes, it is calcite. Calcite is the only mineral to fizz with an acid.

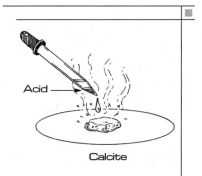

Special Safety Consideration: Hydrochloric acid, even in weak solution, is caustic. Wear goggles, gloves, and a labcoat or apron.

Minerals with a definite shape of their own are **crystals.** Crystals are formed as the atoms and molecules that make up substances form internal lattice structures. Although one thinks immediately of diamonds and other precious stones as cut crystals, crystals form naturally into specific geometric patterns.

Materials: sand, sugar, salt, several minerals with visible crystalline shape, magnifying glass

- Using the magnifying glass, look at sand, sugar, salt, and mineral samples to observe their specific crystalline shapes.

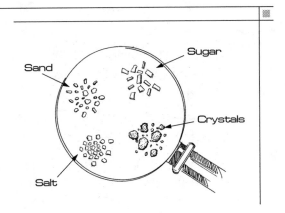

When **igneous rocks** cool slowly, they have larger crystals. Sometimes igneous rocks have such small crystals that they are called texture. Texture is used to identify different igneous rocks such as granite, **rhyolite,** quartz, feldspar, and mica.

Materials: two crucibles, beaker, water, teaspoon, sulfur powder, forceps, Bunsen burner, magnifying glass

- Place a teaspoon (5 mL) of powdered sulfur in one of the crucibles. Allow it to melt and then cool slowly. Place a teaspoon (5 mL) of powdered sulfur in the second crucible. Half-fill the beaker with water. Melt the sulfur and pour it slowly into the beaker. Students will notice that the sulfur that cooled slowly developed larger crystals than the sulfur that cooled rapidly in water.

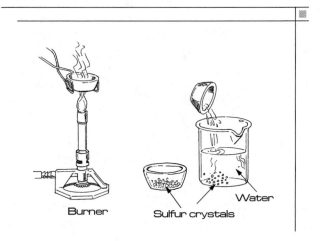

Burner   Sulfur crystals   Water

Special Safety Consideration: Sulfur, while not dangerous, burns with fumes that may be unpleasant, and, in susceptible students, may cause minor respiratory distress. Perform this experiment in a well-ventilated room or in a chemical fume hood.

Sedimentary rocks, as the name implies, are rocks formed from sediments. These **sediments** may be from shells and other hard body parts of animals that live in oceans, such as in limestone. They may be formed of compressed sand and other ocean sediments, as in sandstone. Compressed sediments from freshwater mud and silt make up other sedimentary rocks, such as shale.

Materials: jar, soil, sand, pebbles, gravel, water, teaspoon, paper cup, plaster of Paris

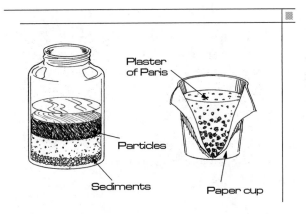

- Place a mix of sand, pebbles, and soil in a jar about half-full of water. Stir vigorously and let the mixture stand for a while. Students will notice that the heavier materials settle to the bottom. They are the sediments. The materials that settle on the top are smaller and lighter. They are the particles.

- Mix some pebbles and gravel with some plaster of Paris. Fill the paper cup with the mixture and let it harden. Peel away the paper cup and observe the sedimentary rock.

Sedimentary rock is created in two major ways, either by the compacting of loose material over time or the crystallization of dissolved minerals. When water evaporates, the dissolved sediments contained within the water crystallize.

Materials: salt, beaker, tablespoon, water, evaporation dish, hot plate

- Half-fill the beaker with water, and dissolve several tablespoons (30–45 mL) of salt. Heat the dish until all the water evaporates. What is left behind is a sedimentary rock: **halite.** Limestone and halite are examples of sedimentary rocks formed by evaporation. Limestone contains calcite.

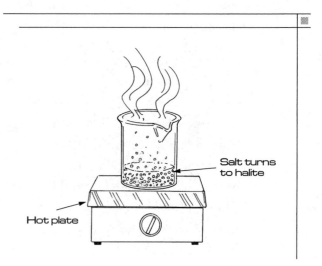

Salt turns to halite

Hot plate

Underground caves have iciclelike formations hanging from the ceiling and standing on the floor. **Stalactites** hang down, while **stalagmites** project upward. Sometimes they join and become solid columns. These sedimentary rocks are calcite formations. They are formed by the dripping and evaporating of calcite-rich water over very long periods of time.

Materials: two beakers, water, Epsom salt, cotton string, small dish

- Fill both beakers nearly three-quarters full of water. Dissolve the Epsom salt until the water is saturated (no more salt will dissolve). Place the two glasses several inches apart. Place the string into both glasses, with a small bow in the middle. Below the middle of the string, place a small dish to catch the dripping.

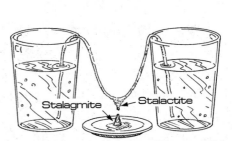

Glasses with water and Epsom salt

In about one day, you will notice your own stalactite and stalagmite.

Limestone is formed when the hard body parts of sea animals, such as mollusks and corals, break apart and are compacted under the pressure of the ocean and bottom sediments. Since the earth is formed of discrete plates, such deposits are eventually thrust upward out of the water. The white cliffs of Dover, for instance, are made almost entirely of limestone. On top of Mt. Etna, a volcano in Sicily, it is possible to find fossilized seashells and limestone deposits.

Materials: **coquina** (time- and pressure-fossilized seashells), seashells, limestone, eyedropper, vinegar

- Place a few drops of vinegar on the shells, coquina, or limestone. Notice the bubbles. The calcium carbonate that is part of the shells, coquina, and limestone react with an acid. Calcium carbonate is the same as the mineral calcite.

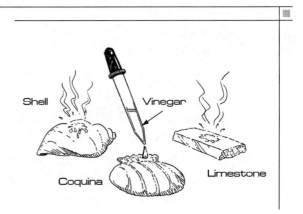

Nothing remains the same on Earth. Changes in water, wind, and temperature break down everything. This breaking down is called **weathering.** Moisture fills the small cracks in rocks, freezes, and breaks down the rocks. Plants and trees grow. As their fine roots enter fine cracks in rocks and then grow, the rocks break.

Materials: small plastic bottle with cap, water, freezer

- Fill the bottle with water, cap it, and place it in the freezer. Notice that the water expands as it becomes ice. Water is a powerful weathering factor when combined with temperature.

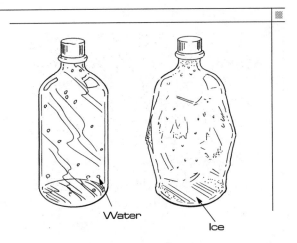

Water

Ice

Another form of weathering is **chemical weathering.** Gases in the air, such as carbon dioxide, nitrogen dioxide, and sulfurs, mix with water and form acids. When it rains, these acids cause the rain to be acid. **Acid rain** kills trees, pollutes streams and lakes, and dissolves marble, limestone, and other rocks. Airborne acids damage nearly all substances they touch. These airborne pollutants are **photochemical** and **thermochemical;** they react with light and heat. The resulting mix is **smog.** Smog has severe health effects on humans and damages most material objects.

Materials: calcium pill, glass, chicken bone, mammalian tooth, vinegar (or a cola beverage)

- Place the calcium pill in the glass and add some vinegar. Notice the chemical reaction: fizzing, foaming, and the breaking of the pill into smaller bits. Eventually these bits will be neutralized by the acid. This activity closely replicates in fast action the effects of chemical weathering.

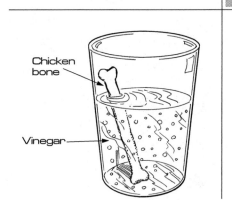

Chicken bone

Vinegar

- Place a chicken bone or tooth in a beaker and add vinegar. You may substitute any cola drink, for it contains phosphoric acid. Show students how, over several days, the bone or tooth is dissolved by the acid.

Water enters the ground through the ground's pores (spaces between its particles). Once water goes under the surface, it becomes **groundwater.** Water continues to go down until it reaches a layer of clay or rock that is impermeable (will not allow water through). If the rock is porous, it becomes saturated with water, and the top of this layer is the **water table.** Shale, a typical sedimentary rock, is made of mud and cemented clay that block water from passing through. **Aquifers,** layers of sand above layers of clay, are a natural reservoir to store runoff water. People tap aquifers for wells. The totality of aquifers in a region is the groundwater basin.

Materials: three large plastic cups or glasses, flask (beaker or glass) with water, clay, gravel, sand

- Fill the three cups with clay, gravel, and sand. Pour a small amount of water into each one. Notice the time it takes for the water to go to the bottom. In gravel the action is fairly rapid, in sand it is slower, while in clay it may be either very slow or nonexistent. The gravel has the largest spaces, sand has smaller but sufficient spaces, and clay has such fine spaces that, if it is compacted, it may be impermeable.

Demo 16
Soil Saturation

Soil will absorb water until all the spaces between its particles are full. When it cannot absorb any more water, it is **saturated.** In terrain such as the Los Angeles basin, where there is much clay near the surface, saturation can present a problem. During rains, after a brief period of saturation, runoff may cause flooding.

Materials: beaker, graduated cylinder, sand, water

- Fill a beaker nearly full with sand. Pour water from the graduated cylinder to fill to the top of the sand. The volume of water in the sand represents the spaces or voids in sand. Now the sand is saturated. Since sand represents soil, this is an example of saturated soil. Any more water you add will rise above the sand and eventually cause runoff or flood from the beaker.

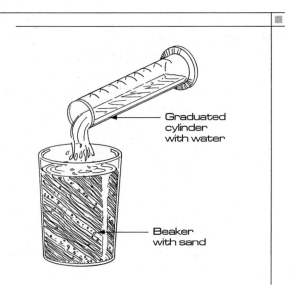

Graduated cylinder with water

Beaker with sand

Water runoff, from mountain springs and rain, works its way into lakes, rivers, and eventually the oceans. Some rainwater percolates— seeps slowly while forcing out air—into the ground, forming aquifers that may be tapped for wells. Many cities line their riverbeds with concrete. Urban structures cover up most of the formerly uncovered soil. Water does not have the opportunity to replenish the dwindling groundwater basin. Most rainfall is lost to runoff.

To save part of the runoff water, the Los Angeles County Flood Control District has established large basins next to rivers, where runoff waters are directed. These spreading basins allow the water to percolate into the aquifers, where it can be stored for future use. As a total strategy, water is kept behind dams and slowly released to the spreading basins unless a storm is announced. Then, by law, the water behind dams must be released to provide storage for the next storm. The purpose of the dams is to slow down the runoff and to conserve water.

Gravity dams, or arch dams, are usually made from either earth or concrete. Dams do not last indefinitely; they continually develop internal cracks due to the earth's movement, thermal expansion of the materials, and other stresses. Engineers and engineering geologists continually maintain and inspect dams. All dams must be government certified for safety. Engineers repair dams by drilling core holes into them to find new cracks. Then, using the same holes, they pump in grout, a mix of cement and water, to fill internal cracks. Some students may have noticed many capped pipes on the surface structure of dams. Now they know why they are there and what they are used for.

(continued)

Materials: three large plastic glasses, graduated cylinder, three different soil samples

- Fill three containers nearly full with soil samples, but do not compact them. Saturate each container and measure carefully how much water is needed to fill each glass to the top. This will provide you with data about soil absorption and percolation rates of the soil samples. You can calculate comparative percolation rates by timing water absorption for the same volume.

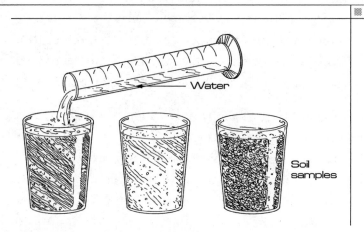

Water

Soil samples

Coastal cities experience the mixing of seawater with their groundwater basin, making water unusable. To prevent this saltwater intrusion into freshwater aquifers, the various water agencies have created a series of wells near the coast. Freshwater is pumped into the wells in large amounts to create a high-pressure barrier. This high-pressure barrier forms a wall that prevents seawater intrusion into the region's groundwater basin. The Los Angeles area has one West Coast Barrier Project in Manhattan Beach and another, the Alamitos Bay Barrier Projects, in the southern region.

Materials: pump, two plastic boxes (with holes drilled for hose), hose, saltwater and freshwater, evaporation dishes or saucers, magnifying glass

- Assemble the pump and hose so that the hose moves through holes drilled in both boxes. Attach the pump to the hose in the freshwater side. Turn on the pump, and pump freshwater through the hose into the saltwater side. When most of the freshwater is gone, pour what is left on the freshwater side into an evaporation dish. Pour some of what is in the saltwater side into another evaporation dish. In a day or two, examine both under a magnifying glass. Which of the two has salt? Which does not?

The motion of water and wind speeds up the long-term effects of
erosion, the wearing away of soil and rock.

Materials: two identical clean quart jars with covers, water,
two pieces of hard candy, measuring cup

- Label one jar as *A*, the other
  as *B*. Put a piece of candy in
  each jar. Pour two cups
  (470 mL) of water over each
  piece of candy. Cover both
  jars. Place them in a location
  where they both can be seen.
  Shake jar *A* once or twice a
  day. Do not disturb jar *B*.
  Notice the difference after
  just two days. The disturbed

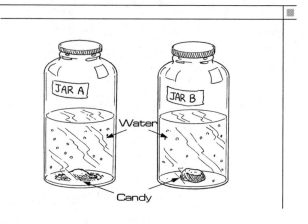

candy has dissolved much more than the undisturbed one.
Mud balls dissolve slowly in rain, but when placed near or
in a stream of fast-moving water, they dissolve faster. The
knocking about by water accelerates erosion.

Rocks beneath waterfalls are slowly eroded by falling water.

Materials: sink with running water, bar of soap, sponge

- Set the bar of soap on the
sponge, and place it under the
faucet. Turn on the faucet and
adjust it to a very fine stream.
The water must fall on the
center of the soap. Let the
water run for 30 to 45
minutes and observe. Where
the water falls, there will be
an indentation. If you let the
water run for a much longer
time, first a hole would

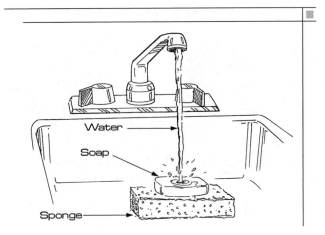

develop and then the entire soap bar would slowly
melt away. (To conserve water, avoid such a prolonged
demonstration.) Rocks are much harder than soap
and are not soluble in water, but the constant hitting
of their surface by water does wear them away.

As the top surfaces of mountains wear away due to erosion, the mountains become lighter and float higher on the earth's mantle. The added weight of erosion sediments causes the seacoast to place additional weight on the mantle. Therefore, it slowly sinks. The up-and-down movement of the earth is **isostasy**.

Materials: 2- × 4- × 4-inch wooden block, glass or plastic see-through container (at least twice the size of the wood), tablespoon, masking tape, water, marker, plastic sandwich bag, sand, ruler

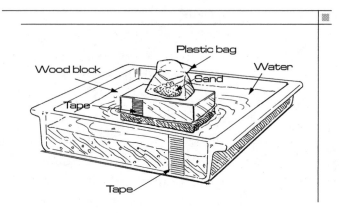

- Place a piece of tape on one side of the wood block, and mark it off in centimeters. Place a piece of tape on one side of the see-through container. Mark it off in centimeters. Half-fill the container with water. Place the block in the water. On top of the block, place the plastic bag with 1 to 2 tablespoons (15–30 mL) of sand. Mark the level of water on both the container and the block. Carefully remove the plastic bag with the sand. Again observe the level of water on the block and the container. The upward movement of the block models the uplift due to erosion (removal of plastic bag with sand).

Glaciers are large, deep (one mile or more) rivers of snow on top of ice. Since they are massive, they melt only slightly in the summer near their surface. Glaciers slowly flow down a slope or valley. As they slowly melt, they drag along **alluvial** materials, byproducts of erosion, such as soil and rock. They create long ridges of alluvial debris called **moraines.**

Materials: sand, soap, ice cube

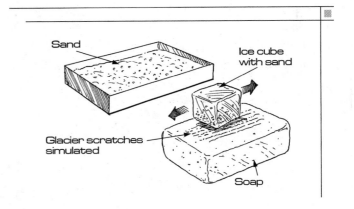

Sand

Ice cube
with sand

Glacier scratches
simulated

Soap

- Place the ice cube in the sand. Then scrape the soap with the ice cube. The scratches in the soap represent the scratches made by glaciers. Scratches such as these on the walls and floor of a valley are clues to the presence of ancient glaciers. The bottom glacier ice, while moving, trapped much debris, including many rocks. These rocks caused the scratches on the walls and floor of a valley.

Wind causes erosion—the moving away of the earth's surface materials. If the material is sand, the wind forms sand dunes, or hills of sand. These dunes have two sides: the **windward** side that faces the wind and the **leeward** side that faces away from the wind. The windward side has a gentle slope, while the leeward has a steeper slope. From the slope of a sand dune, you can tell the direction of the winds that formed it.

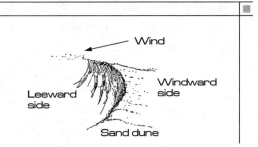

Materials: sand, large piece of cardboard, water

- Make two small mountains of sand on the cardboard. Sprinkle water over one. Blow air over both. Help students notice how the dry mountain was moved away by the movement of air. This demonstrates wind erosion.

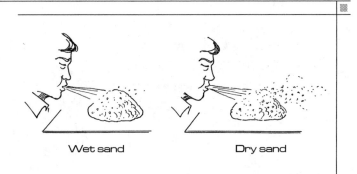

Wind blowing over water surfaces causes waves. Their size depends on the wind speed. The top of the wave is a crest, while the bottom is a **trough.** The distance from either the crest or the trough to the water surface is wave height (amplitude). The greater the wave height, the greater the wave energy.

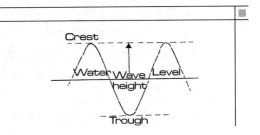

Materials: shallow pan (clear plastic is best), water, overhead projector (optional)

- Blow air over a shallow pan of water to cause waves. Bottom-lit projection may show waves on the overhead, if you use a transparent pan.

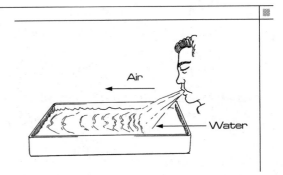

Rivers have a life cycle, almost like living things. Since water tends to seek its own level, rivers move from mountaintops toward the ocean. The young river exists in the high mountains, where the water moves very fast. This region is called the **headwater** of the river. Lower down the mountain, the middle-aged river slows down and spreads out. It may move in lazy s-shapes called **meanders.** If the s-shape is tight enough, occasionally the two sides of the "s" come together and form a small lakelike area called an **oxbow.** Even further downstream, as the river meets the ocean, the river spreads out into a wide region called a **delta.** It is called a delta because the shape of the river at this point looks like the Greek letter Δ, pronounced *delta*. The river in its old age moves very slowly in a delta, and may mix with salt water, creating a **brackish** ecosystem, a swampy mix of fresh and saline waters. In the following experiment, you will look at the speed of a river in each of the three regions: headwater, meander, and delta.

Materials: inclined plane and flat region covered with clay, small stones, water, glitter, basin, pitcher

Procedure:

1. Create your "riverbed" based on what you now know about river life cycles. In the headwater, for instance, create straight dropping streams with small rocks in the riverbed. In the middle of the river, create meanders and an oxbow or two, and create the wide, flat, triangular shape of the delta. Place the basin at the base of the delta to catch water as it enters the "ocean."

2. Add some glitter to the water, and slowly pour the water into the streams of the headwater region. The glitter represents silt washed down from the mountains.

3. Observe the progression of the glitter as the river slows.

Conclusion: What happens to the glitter at the delta of your model? How does this demonstration reflect what you have noticed or learned about rivers? Why do you think rivers behave in this fashion?

Wind, water, glaciers, temperature, and chemical reactions cause erosion. The materials of erosion are carried by rivers into the oceans. The river water dissolves many minerals and then mixes with the salty ocean water, adding more minerals to the seawater.

Materials: seawater, beaker, hot plate, salt, Bunsen burner, wire loop (platinum wire, if available), forceps, oven mitt

- Half-fill a beaker with seawater. If you do not have seawater, prepare a saturated solution of water with salt. (Mix as much salt as the water will dissolve.) Boil off the water, and you will find a whitish crystalline residue in the beaker. These are the minerals dissolved in seawater. Test the residue (as described below) for the presence of salt.

- The flame test is used to identify salt. Sodium chloride (NaCl)—ordinary salt—is the most common mineral dissolved in the ocean. Sodium glows, when heated, with a rich, bright-yellow color. Make a wire loop, place on it some table salt, and place it over the flame. Use forceps to hold the wire. Platinum wire is preferred but not essential. The flame will glow bright yellow.

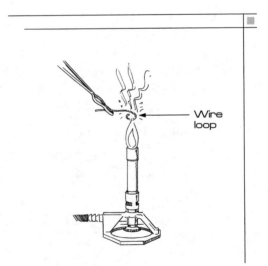

- Dip the wire loop in the seawater residue and repeat the flame test. What color is the flame?

Sedimentary rocks are usually formed in horizontal layers. Many times these rock layers show in cross section that they are bent upwards, as if folded at many different angles. Apparently, pressures in the earth's crust caused the layers to move upward. The movement of the earth is gradual and invisible except during a **tectonic event,** such as an earthquake or a volcanic eruption. The earth's movement can cause an uplift, a drop, a sideslip, or a combination of these. The earth's movements and earthquakes are caused by the motion of the earth's **tectonic plates,** moving sections of the earth's crust or mantle. Marine fossils that have been found on mountains thousands of feet high are evidence of this movement. The ancient city of Tehuanaca, in South America, has all the semblance of a seaport, yet it is over 10,000 feet above sea level.

Materials: several sheets of colored paper

- Assemble a stack of many sheets of colored paper, each representing a layer. Take the entire stack and press together, causing the center to bulge upward (uplift). This demonstrates the folding of rock layers.

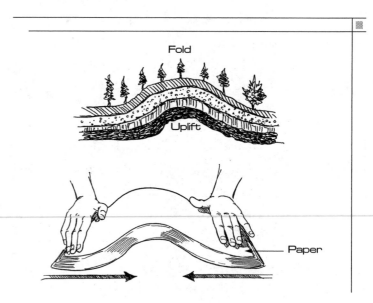

Many animals lived on Earth before humans made an appearance. At the very outside, humans, and their immediate ancestors, hominids, have existed on the planet for only 7 million years. Life, however, has existed here since shortly after the planet formed and cooled. The earliest fossil evidence of life is dated at 3.1 billion years ago. Any life on Earth that existed before the time when humans began making written records is called prehistoric. There were prehistoric humans, of course. Mammoths, dinosaurs, and saber-toothed cats are examples of prehistoric animals. Scientists learn about prehistoric animals from **fossils:** bones, footprints, shells, and actual animals or plants. The majority of fossils are found in sedimentary rocks, which at some time were under the ocean. Water entering the rock may have dissolved the bones, but their impression remained in the rock. If this impression was filled with minerals and other debris, the filler formed the exact copy of the original bone, animal, or shell. This is called the cast. Fossils normally take many years to form, but you can demonstrate the basic process overnight.

Materials: seashell or small bone, clay, small containers (such as 8-oz milk boxes), mixing beaker, plaster of Paris, water, teaspoon

- Make your own fossil overnight. Place the clay on the bottom of one small container. Press into it the shell or bone, making a mold. Remove the shell or bone. In the mixing beaker, prepare some plaster of Paris by adding water and mixing until it is creamy and barely flowing. Pour the plaster of Paris into the mold, the impression of the shell or bone. Let the plaster harden overnight. Gently tap and remove the fossil cast the next day.

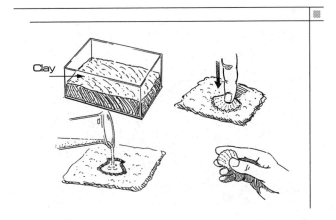

Clay

Over Earth's 4.1 billion-year history, the planet has been struck by **meteors** and comets countless times. Some of the impacts of these strikes caused great upheaval of the land, as well as mass extinctions. Most of the impact sites have been lost over the years as the processes of life and geological events have filled in the **craters.** However, some sites, like the Berringer crater in the American Southwest, are still visible today.

In this experiment, you will look at what effect a meteor impact has on various kinds of soil.

Materials: 2 shallow basins at least 30 cm square (cat litter boxes work well), enough soil and sand to fill each basin, a sprinkling of flour and cocoa, ruler, pen or pencil, several pebbles of various sizes, graph paper, balance

Procedure:

1. Fill one box with soil, and one box with sand. Sprinkle the top of the soil box with flour; sprinkle the top of the sand box with cocoa. This will help you see the impacts better.

2. Choose a small pebble, determine its mass, and have one student drop the pebble from eye level into the soil-filled basin.

3. Measure the crater, and make a note of the depth and width of the crater, along with the mass of the pebble. Repeat the same process with the box of sand.

4. Predict what will occur if you select a larger pebble, then try it again, recording all the same types of data.

5. Next, select a medium-sized pebble and drop it into the soil, and then drop it into the sand. Record all relevant data.

(continued)

6. Create two graphs for the soil box. In the first graph, graph mass on the x-axis, and crater depth on the y-axis. In the second, graph mass on the x-axis and crater depth on the y-axis. Then, create a similar pair of graphs for the data from the box of sand.

Conclusion: How do the graphs differ? What can you say about cratering in different media? What role does the mass of the meteor play?

Fossil fuels were formed in the Carboniferous Period of prehistoric time from the remains of living things. Common fossil fuels are coal, natural gas, and liquid petroleum. Charcoal, a form of the element carbon, is formed when materials burn and lack sufficient oxygen to totally oxidize (burn).

Materials: test tube, test-tube holder, stand, Bunsen burner, wood splints, matches

- Place several wood splints in a test tube and secure the test tube with a stand. Tip the test tube up slightly. Heat the test tube until the splints inside turn black. While this process is ongoing, take a lighted splint and place it at the mouth of the test tube. It will flare up because the byproduct of changing the wood into charcoal is a gas similar to natural gas.

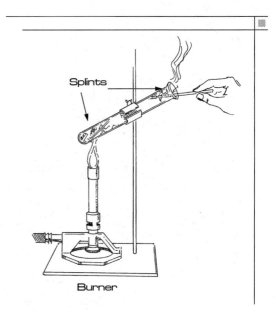

Splints

Burner

The atmosphere is the 500-mile-high ocean of air surrounding Earth. Most of Earth's air molecules are concentrated in the lower 75 miles of the atmosphere. As one goes higher, air pressure drops and the air is less dense. Air has substance and takes up space. Air is a mixture of several gases:

1. Nitrogen 78%

2. Oxygen 21%

3. Argon 0.94%

4. Carbon dioxide 0.04%

5. Helium, krypton, neon, xenon 0.02%

Materials: large plastic bag

- Fill the plastic bag with air, seal it, and feel how air fills the bag. Air does occupy space.

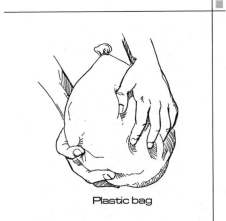

Plastic bag

Materials: balloon, balance

- Inflate the balloon with air and place it on the balance. Balance it. Release the air and place the balloon back on the balance. It will be lighter. This proves that air has mass.

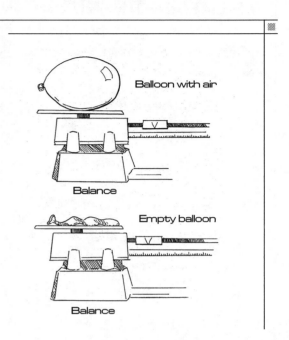

Balloon with air

Balance

Empty balloon

Balance

To have a fire, one needs three ingredients: fuel, oxygen, and kindling temperature.

Materials: small aluminum dish or pie tin, birthday candle, water, empty jar, matches

- Light the candle and drip some wax into the dish. Then place the burning candle in the wax so that it stays upright. Fill the dish with water. Cover the candle with the jar. Notice that the candle goes out after a short while. It has used up all the oxygen in the jar. Fire needs oxygen.

- Remove the jar and relight the candle. Wet your fingers. Squeeze the flame of the candle. It goes out. You have deprived the flame of essential oxygen.

Materials: aluminum dish or pie tin, water, graduated cylinder, small candle, matches

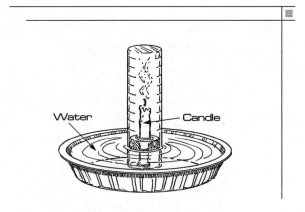

Water   Candle

- Light the candle and drip several drops of candle wax into the plate. Then place the burning candle in the wax so that it stays upright. Fill the dish nearly full of water. Place the inverted graduated cylinder over the candle. Notice the level of water inside the cylinder. After a short time, the candle goes out. Notice how the water has risen inside the graduated cylinder. The rise is about one fifth or about 20% of the inside volume of gas. This confirms that oxygen makes up 21% of air.

Materials: test tube, tongs, limewater, small piece of paper, matches

Limewater is commercially available; however, it can easily be made in the classroom. To do so, mix 1.5 g (or .05 oz) $Ca(OH)_2$(s) per liter (or 4.25 cups) of water. Stir or shake vigorously, and allow the solids to settle overnight. When using limewater, decant carefully to avoid transferring any solid or suspended $Ca(OH)_2$(s). Limewater turns cloudy in the presence of carbon dioxide, although it appears clear naturally.

- Place a small piece of lit paper in the mouth of a test tube containing limewater. Hold the test tube with tongs and gently agitate the test tube. Observe how the limewater turns milky. This indicates the presence of carbon dioxide, a byproduct of fire.

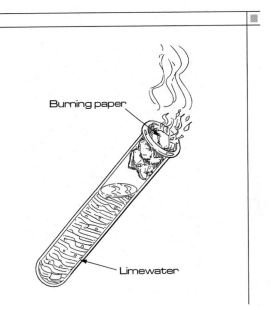

Burning paper

Limewater

When heat is added to objects, molecules begin to vibrate faster and move farther apart. The heat energy is transferred from molecule to molecule. This is **conduction** of heat. Earth, after being warmed by the sun, passes its heat by conduction to the air.

Materials: Bunsen burner, piece of metal or old silverware

- Heat a strip of metal or an old piece of silverware on one end and have students notice how the other end becomes gradually warmer.

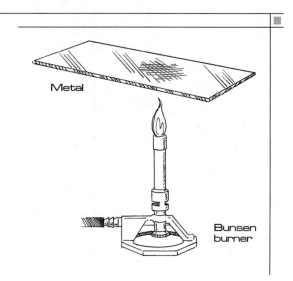

Metal

Bunsen burner

Special Safety Consideration: Metal conducts heat very rapidly. Make sure any student who is going to touch the metal does so early in the heating process to avoid burns.

The sun emits many forms of energy that travel out to the universe in waves. Among the many energy forms are invisible **infrared rays,** which have longer wavelengths than visible light. These are rays of heat energy. Emitting heat energy in waves is a method of heat transfer called **radiation.**

Materials: light with bulb

- Turn on the lightbulb and let it glow for a few minutes. Have your students feel the heat radiated by the bulb.

Special Safety Consideration: Students should avoid coming into contact with the hot bulb, which can cause burns.

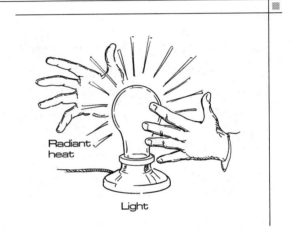

Radiant heat

Light

Materials: lamp with heat bulb, glass of water, thermometer

- Place the lamp with heat bulb above the glass of water. Place the thermometer in the glass. Notice the water temperature. Let the heat from the bulb heat the water. Take the temperature every few minutes to show a change.

Special Safety Consideration:
If using a mercury thermometer, be aware of the proper clean-up and disposal procedure if the thermometer happens to break.

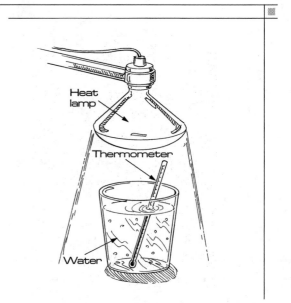

Heat lamp

Thermometer

Water

A **radiometer** is a small device, available at most science and nature stores, that consists of a glass globe with a small pinwheel inside. Each of the vanes on the pinwheel is white on one side and black on the other. Since white tends to reflect light and heat, while black absorbs it, the black vanes absorb heat and light energy and push the pinwheel in circles as the black sides heat up and cool down repeatedly.

An infrared passing filter is a filter that does not permit visible light to transmit but allows longer wavelengths through.

Materials: radiometer, light with bulb, infrared passing filter

- Place the radiometer a few inches from the light bulb. Show students how the radiometer spins around when exposed to the light and heat of the light bulb. Next, show students how the infrared passing filter blocks all visible light and prevents them from seeing the bulb at all. Now, place the infrared passing filter between the light and the radiometer. The radiometer will continue to turn, even though no light reaches it. This demonstrates that there must be some other form of energy, invisible to the eye, that reaches the radiometer and makes it move. This energy is infrared rays—a form of heat.

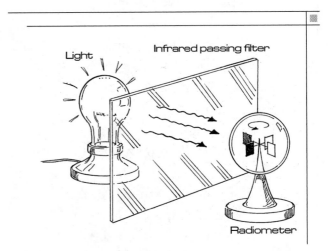

Light

Infrared passing filter

Radiometer

Warm air rises, causing air currents, or winds. Warm-water streams move through the oceans and make ocean currents. The rising of warmer substances and the sinking of cooler ones is **convection.** Warmer substances are lighter because their molecules are farther apart, and fewer molecules occupy the space compared with cooler substances. This lessening of mass makes the substances more buoyant (able to float) in air or water.

Materials: two large paper shopping bags, string, adhesive tape, two metersticks, lamp

- Hang the two inverted (upside-down) shopping bags from the ends of one meterstick with string. Balance the bags so that they are as far apart as possible. Hang this meterstick at its center of balance from another meterstick that rests between two student desks. Place the lamp 20 cm below one bag and turn on the lamp. As the heat from the bulb heats up the air in the bag, the bag will appear to become lighter and will rise.

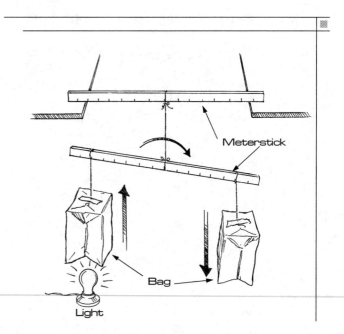

Meterstick

Bag

Light

Ocean water is warmest near the surface and gets colder with depth, forming a thermal gradient. Different temperature zones have unique animal and plant life because oceanic inhabitants are temperature sensitive. On maps, contours with the same temperatures are **thermoclines.** One of the best-known oceanic currents is the Gulf Stream. It begins in the Gulf of Mexico, flows northeastward across the Atlantic, and passes by and warms up the coasts of West Africa and Western Europe.

Materials: fish tank nearly full of water, food coloring, convection jar, hot water, florist clay or glue gun

Note: A convection jar can be made from a baby food jar. Punch two holes in its lid and insert the cylindrical portions of two plastic eyedroppers. Insert one to be as deep as the jar and place the other above the lid. Seal them with florist clay or a heat-melt glue gun. Prepare several jars for later use.

- Fill the convection jar with warm water and add several drops of food coloring. Cover the jar, and place it gently on the bottom of the fish tank. (A large transparent jar can be used as a substitute for the fish tank.) You will observe immediate convection currents as the colored water moves upwards. This activity is visible both in the tank and inside the convection bottle. Later, you may wish to repeat the demonstration, using a different color. Soon you will have a water tank with colored layers to represent thermoclines.

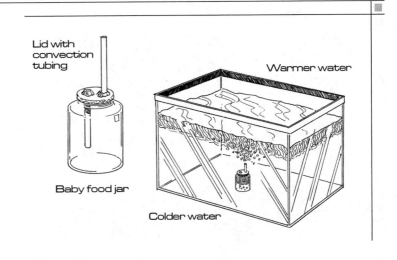

Lid with convection tubing

Warmer water

Baby food jar

Colder water

Thermal inversion develops when warm air masses form a blanketlike cover over colder air masses. The trapped underlying air masses become polluted and, through **photochemical** and **thermochemical** reaction (the chemicals in the air react with sunshine and heat), smog develops. Smog is a major ecological and health problem of most large cities.

Use the previous demonstration (39), Warm Water Rises: Convection, to illustrate how layers can become trapped.

Smog got its name from the joining of two words, *smoke* and *fog*, during the Victorian era in London, when, during a particularly bad winter, a combination of factory smoke and London fog killed hundreds of people. Today, we typically think of smog as a phenomenon caused by industrial and automotive emissions that is held close to the surface of the planet in certain regions by inversion layers—cooler upper air that holds down warm, dirty air.

Indeed, auto emissions are one of the largest modern smog producers. When the sun shines or when the air is warm, the combination of chemicals—mainly CO (carbon dioxide) and NO_2 (nitrogen dioxide)—turn a characteristically dirty brown color. That is why smog tends to be worse in summer months than in winter months.

Today, you are going to capture some automobile emissions, with help from a teacher, and turn what seems like an invisible gas into the smog we all know and fear.

Materials: test tube with rubber stopper, automobile (run by your teacher), hot water, forceps

Procedure:

1. Ask your teacher to start his or her car. Take a deep breath, away from the car, and hold your breath in. Take a test tube and place the opening right next to the car's tailpipe, while holding your breath. Quickly stopper the tube. Move away from the car and breathe.

2. Back in the classroom, look at the test tube in sunlight. There may be a little bit of carbon noticeable, but not a lot.

3. Now, holding the test tube with forceps under hot running water, watch the color of the gas slowly change to a dull brown. In extremely warm weather, or when exposed to sunlight for long periods, gases emitted from the tailpipe into the atmosphere would also turn this color.

(continued)

4. After everyone has had a chance to view the smog, release it outdoors.

Conclusion: What causes smog to change color? What are the implications of millions of automobiles all producing CO and NO_2?

Special Safety Consideration: Carbon monoxide is dangerous to breathe in large quantities. Be sure you do not inhale smoke from the tailpipe while collecting the gases.

The sun heats up Earth's landmasses and oceans. The weather and climate on Earth are directly dependent on this heat energy transfer, and so are all the phenomena that accompany weather, such as winds, tornadoes, hurricanes, rain, snow, and ocean waves. Continental masses heat up and cool more quickly than water masses. During the day, flat lands are colder than the adjacent hills. Air flows from the valleys to the hills, from a region of higher pressure to one of lower pressure, causing a valley breeze. At night, the hills are colder than the valley, and the reverse occurs. The cooler mountain air flows down to the valleys, causing a mountain breeze.

Materials: two identical containers, soil, water, two thermometers, lamp (optional)

- Fill both containers about three-quarters full—one with soil and the other with water. Place a thermometer in both. Place both containers in sunshine or under a lamp. Measure the temperatures of both at the start, and again, after about 25 minutes. The soil will be warmer than the water.

Water   Soil

Icebergs, even though they are often born out of seawater, are made entirely of freshwater. Freezing chemically squeezes salt out of water. When an iceberg or any other sea ice melts, it takes a long time for the freshwater to mix with the salt water of the ocean. The salt water is denser than freshwater, so they tend not to mix until wave action finally mixes them up.

If a large frozen iceberg happens to be in the neighborhood, however, and it is colder than the surrounding fresh- or saltwater layers, it causes a density change in the water. Even freshwater, chilled to near freezing, is denser than the warmer saltwater below the surface, and will consequently sink. When this happens, an ocean current is born. Currents that are related to the interplay of salt and temperature in the ocean are called **thermohaline** currents. In the following experiment, you will demonstrate such a scenario.

Materials: glass loaf pan, 30 mL salt, blue food coloring, ice cubes

Procedure:

1. Mix 30 mL (2 tbsp) of salt and a liter of water in a glass loaf pan.

2. Put the pan in the freezer until chips of ice begin to form on the surface.

3. Remove the pan, and drop a few drops of blue food coloring on the surface. Watch and see what happens as the surface "sea ice" melts.

4. Now, place an ice cube at one end of the pan. Watch for a few minutes.

Conclusion: What happened when the ice cube entered the pan? What causes the currents you can see in the glass loaf pan?

Different materials need different amounts of heat energy to rise to the same temperature. Temperature is a measure of heat in a material and, indirectly, a measure of molecular speed.

Materials: three identical pint jars, powdered iron, sand, water (or your choice of materials), three thermometers

- Half-fill all three containers with powdered iron, sand, and water. Place a thermometer in each container, and expose them to the sun. Measure the temperatures after 25 minutes. The iron will have the highest temperature, next will be the sand, and next, the water. In more advanced science, the amount of heat absorption is **specific heat capacity.** Every material has its own specific heat capacity.

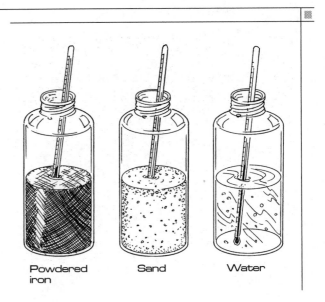

Powdered iron   Sand   Water

The pressure of air is exerted in all directions. In the following activities, some students may erroneously assume that surface tension holds the cardboard in place.

Materials: glass, water, sheet of cardboard, sink or basin

- Fill a glass with water to the brim. Then place a sheet of cardboard on it. Invert and notice how the water does not fall out. The pressure of air keeps the cardboard in place. Do this demonstration over a sink or basin, just in case of problems.

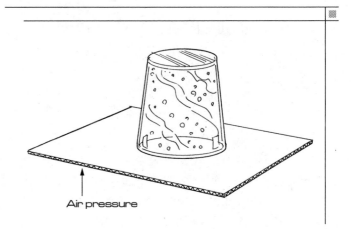

Air pressure

When energy is unbalanced (higher versus lower pressure), whether it is osmotic, electrical (voltage), or physical (air pressure), energy flows from the region of higher pressure to the lower one until a balance (equilibrium) is attained. If a space capsule loses its pressure integrity, life-supporting air escapes out to the vacuum of space with fatal consequences for the spacefarers. On planet Earth, the pressure of the atmosphere is 14.7 pounds per square inch. This pressure is sufficient to crush any container with vacuum inside it, unless it is specifically designed to withstand these forces.

Materials: shelled hard-boiled egg, birthday candle, large bottle or jar (with mouth barely smaller than the egg), matches

- Insert the candle into either end of the egg and light it. Place the candle inside the bottle and seal the opening with the egg. As the candle burns the oxygen, 21% of the inside gas, the bottle will have a region of lower pressure. Eventually the egg will squeeze into the bottle. Be careful to use one hand only, as soon as you have positioned the egg, so that students can see how things happen.

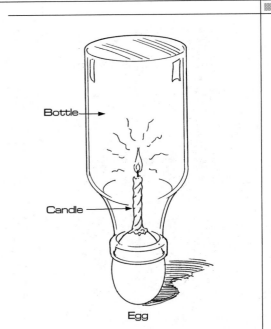

Bottle

Candle

Egg

- To remove the egg, hold the bottle with its opening down at an angle and blow air into it. As you blow, gravity will hold the egg at the opening, maintaining a seal. The air above the egg will gain more pressure and will push the egg out.

Materials: empty soda can, tablespoon, small pan, water, forceps, Bunsen burner

- Place a tablespoon (15 mL) of water into an empty soda can. Fill the pan nearly full of water. Heat the soda can with forceps over a Bunsen burner until steam begins to escape from the pop-top. Rapidly invert the can and place its top in the pan of water. The heated air inside the can will have fewer molecules, and therefore less pressure, than the surrounding air. There should be enough air pressure difference for the surrounding air pressure to crush the can.

The normal pressure of air will crush any container that has vacuum inside it, unless it is built to withstand air pressure of 14.7 pounds per square inch.

Materials: Bunsen burner, tablespoon, small amount of water, string, stand with ring, empty gallon can (The can needs to be clean and free of chemicals on the inside, preferably new.)

- Do the following steps in order:

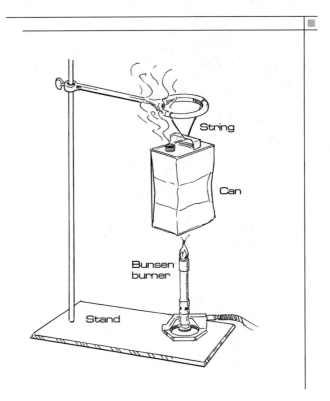

1. Tie a piece of string to the can. Then hang the can from the ring.

2. Place the ring high enough to allow for the Bunsen burner.

3. Place a tablespoon (15 mL) of water inside the can.

4. Heat the can until white vapor starts coming out from the can. While heating, move the burner around, so no part of the can burns through.

5. Stop heating. Quickly close the can with its lid.

6. Let it stand. Spin it lightly. The can will implode gradually.

7. To speed up the process, cool the can by spraying it with water. This will cause water to condense inside the can, further thinning its air.

Special Safety Consideration: Do not use a can that has previously held flammable liquids.

The pressure of air can hold up a column of water almost 34 feet high (almost 10 meters). This is true at sea level at standard temperature and pressure (STP). At higher altitudes, the pressure drops, since there is less air above. The lowering of air pressure lowers the boiling point of liquids. Certain foods that will cook at 100°C at sea level will remain uncooked despite long cooking times in the mountains. Pressure cookers help in these situations. By increasing the internal pot pressure, pressure cookers increase the boiling point and allow foods to be cooked more quickly. Pressure caps on car radiators increase the boiling point of the coolant. The caps allow car cooling fluids to boil at higher temperatures. The coolants can therefore absorb more heat energy from the engine before boiling over.

Materials: glass, large container, water

- Fill the container nearly full of water. Place the glass in the container, submerge it, and make sure that the glass is full of water. Invert the glass and pull it gently up from the water, but stop before you reach the top edges of the glass. The water will stay on the inside of the glass due to the pressure of air.

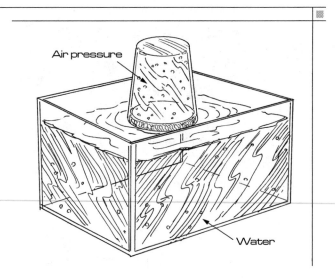

Air pressure

Water

An **aneroid barometer,** a device to measure air pressure, does not contain any liquid. It is usually made from a small can with one very thin side that moves in or out with the slightest changes in air pressure. A pointer is connected to this thin part of the can, and it points along a scale. The aneroid barometer in this demonstration is easy to assemble. It consists of a vacuum-packed coffee can and a pointer that magnifies the subtle caving in or expansion of the can. It is a mechanical amplifier.

Rising air pressure is a predictor of fair weather, while dropping pressure indicates bad weather. You may either calibrate your barometer against another one or listen to weather forecasts for your reference points. In making your own weather forecasts include data other than air pressure, such as temperature, moisture, and clouds.

Materials: one piece of 1- × 6- × 36-inch board (the base), 1- × 2- × 12-inch stick (scale support), 1/4-inch dowel 33 inches in length (pivoting pointer), pin (pointer tip), 1- × 1- × 12-inch stick (pivot upright), unopened can of coffee or any other vacuum-packed product (of similar size), wood glue, screws, 6-inch-long stiff wire, soldering iron, solder, drill, measuring tape, pencil

- Do the following steps in order:

1. Mark the centerline on the base board. (Carefully examine the illustration.)

2. Fasten the coffee can securely on the centerline by gluing its bottom or securing it with screws overlapping the bottom rim (without breaking the vacuum of the can).

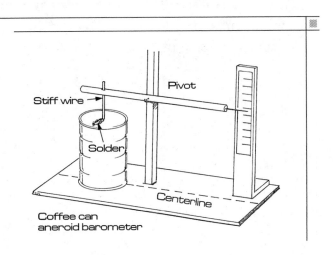

Coffee can aneroid barometer

(continued)

3. Take the piece of stiff wire and bend it into the shape of an *L*. Solder the short end to the center of the coffee can, so that the longer end is perpendicular to the top of the can.

4. Fasten the upright stick one-eighth of an inch off center to act as a pivot arm support.

5. Drill a hole about three inches from one end of the dowel. Secure the dowel into the pivot arm support with a screw. Make certain that the pivot arm (the dowel) is free to move and installed on the centerline.

6. Install the scale support on the opposite end of the board. Offset it from the centerline to allow the pivot arm to move freely. Secure it with wood glue and a screw from below.

7. Place the pin on the end of the pivot arm to act as a pointer.

8. Connect the stiff wire to the pivot arm in the horizontal position.

9. Make a scale using the measuring tape to mark increments. Fasten it on the support.

Special Safety Consideration: Use of the tools in this experiment can be hazardous. Do not allow students to use drills, soldering irons, or other dangerous tools.

Our Earth's **atmosphere** is held next to the planet's surface by gravity. When we measure atmospheric pressure, we are in fact measuring the weight of all the air above us. When atmospheric pressure is high, it usually means water in the air will remain a vapor, and we'll have sunny weather. When there is low pressure, the water vapor in the air turns to tiny liquid droplets, and we have cloudy weather. When the droplets stick together, we might even have rain. You can build a barometer, which is the instrument that is used to measure atmospheric pressure.

Materials: glass jar with a wide mouth (like a pickle jar), balloon, scissors, rubber cement, straw, tape, pencil and paper

Procedure:

1. Cut off the thick neck of the balloon. Brush a little rubber cement around the rim of the jar, and stretch the balloon over the jar so that there is a nearly flat piece of rubber.

2. Tape the straw to the balloon with one end of the straw right in the center of the jar and a long piece going out over the edge of the jar.

3. Watch the jar during periods of unsettled weather and fine weather. In unsettled weather, the air pressure in the jar will be higher than the outside atmosphere, and the balloon will rise, causing the straw to point down. In fine weather, the opposite will occur.

Conclusion: What do you notice about changes in the weather and the barometer? Can you predict a change? Why?

If you take a square inch and go upwards for 500 miles, you will have a volume of air 500 miles high and one square inch wide. The total mass of this air is 14.7 pounds. Air exerts a pressure of 14.7 pounds per square inch at the bottom of Earth's atmosphere (sea level). If you go to the mountains, the air column becomes shorter, and therefore there is less mass and less air pressure.

1 inch square

500 miles

14.7 pounds

Materials: three or four bricks, marker, ruler

- Ask one student who is wearing white, smooth-soled shoes to volunteer for this demonstration. Ask the student to sit in front of the class and place his or her foot on a desk, so that everyone can see the sole of the shoe. Draw a one-inch square on the sole.

- Now that everyone has seen one square inch, have the students line up and pass each other the stack of bricks. Point out that the weight of the bricks is similar to the weight of 500 miles of atmosphere causing 14.7 pounds per square inch on every part of our bodies.

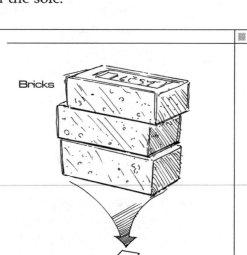

Bricks

The direction of the wind is an important component of weather. Airports have air socks and wind vanes. Weather forecasters launch helium balloons to find the direction of wind. By combining the wind vane with a compass, one can establish wind direction. You may wish to mount the assembled vane on the roof or other elevated place at your school.

Materials: wheel from a roller skate or a skateboard, dowel, 3-inch bolt (fits inside wheel hub), three nuts, two wood screws, two large washers, aluminum sheet metal (or pie tin), small wood base (6 × 6 inches)

- Do the following steps in order:

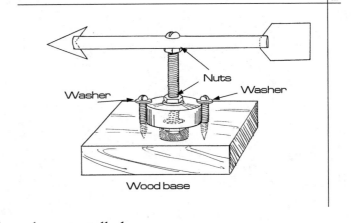

1. See illustration for help.

2. In the center of the wood base, drill a hole wider and deeper than the bolt with a nut on it. The bolt must be able to turn freely in this hole after all the nuts have been installed.

3. Prepare an arrow and a tail from the aluminum sheeting or pie plate. Assemble the weather vane by attaching the arrow and the tail to the dowel. For best results, make the tail at least twice the size of the pointer. Drill a hole in the dowel and place it on the bolt. Install a nut to fasten this assembly to the bolt head. Mount the support bolt in the center of the wheel, with nuts on both sides.

4. Mount the skate wheel centered over the hole in the base, so that the assembly can turn freely. The wheel will have a real ball bearing for ease of turning.

5. Mount the wheel with screws and large washers.

(continued)

6. Occasionally oil the wheel.

Note: A less sensitive wind vane can be built using a small block, a stick, some cardboard for the arrow and tail, a center pivot made with a nail and washers above and below the stick. This primitive model will work only in more substantial winds.

Special Safety Consideration: Some of the tools used in this demonstration can be hazardous. Do not allow students to use drills.

Water exists in the atmosphere in the form of gas, or water vapor. Most of it comes from the **evaporation,** or changing of liquid to vapor, of the oceans. Plants and animals add water to the air. Animals add water to the environment through respiration, breath. Plants add water to the air through the process of **transpiration,** the release of water vapor from pores on the undersides of their leaves.

Materials: plant, plastic bag, sponge, water, mirror, coffeepot

- Breathe on a mirror. Show the **condensation,** the liquid removed from a vapor, of your breath.

- Demonstrate evaporation: Moisten a sponge and wet your chalkboard. Let students observe how the wet streak dries up.

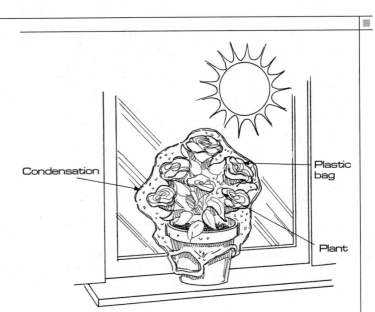

Condensation

Plastic bag

Plant

- Demonstrate transpiration: Cover a plant with a plastic bag, place it in the sun for about 15 minutes, and observe the moisture condensing on the inside.

- Lift the lid of a heated coffeepot and show the water vapor going up.

The amount of water vapor in the air around us is humidity. Since air can hold varying amounts of water, the true amount of water in the air is **absolute humidity.** The amount of water present in the air compared to the maximum amount possible is **relative humidity.** High relative humidity can make people uncomfortable because their perspiration will not evaporate; they feel warmer than they would at the same temperature in less-humid conditions. When the temperature is adjusted for the relative humidity, it is **apparent temperature.**

Using the temperature and humidity from your local weather station, convert your temperature to apparent temperature, using the table below. If the air temperature is 30°C and the relative humidity is 60%, the apparent temperature is 32.2°C. Some weather forecasts also refer to the apparent temperature as the comfort index or heat index (HI).

APPARENT TEMPERATURE C° CHART

Relative Humidity	Actual Air Temperature										
	21	**24**	**27**	**30**	**32**	**35**	**38**	**41**	**43**	**46**	**49**
0%	17.5	20.1	22.9	25.5	28.3	30.5	32.8	35	37.2	39.4	41.6
10%	18.3	21	23.9	26.6	29.4	32.2	35	37.8	40.6	43.9	46.7
20%	18.9	22.2	25	27.7	30.5	33.9	37.2	40.6	44.4	48.9	54.4
30%	19.4	22.8	25.5	28.8	32.2	35.6	40	45	50.6	57.2	64.4
40%	20	23.3	26.1	30	33.9	38.3	43.3	50.6	58.3	66.1	
50%	20.5	23.9	27.2	31.1	35.6	41.7	48.9	57.2	65.6		
60%	21	24.4	27.8	32.2	37.7	45.6	55.6	65			
70%	21	25	30	33.9	41.1	51.1	62.2				
80%	21.6	25.5	30	36.1	45	57.8					
90%	21.6	26.1	31.1	38.9	50						
100%	22.2	27	32.3	42.2							

The relative humidity measurement is made with a **psychrometer.**
The instrument consists of two thermometers on a board that can
be spun around (assembly described below). The bulb of one of
the thermometers is covered by wet cotton. When the instrument
is spun, the water of the wet bulb will evaporate. The rate of
its evaporation will be a function of the humidity of air. As
water evaporates, it will cool the thermometer. By knowing the
temperature of the dry thermometer and the difference between the
dry and wet thermometer temperatures, one can find out the relative
humidity by using the chart that follows.

Materials: small board, two thermometers, glue, small amount
of cotton cloth, tiny rubber band, small handle (dowel), screw,
screwdriver

- Do the following steps in order:

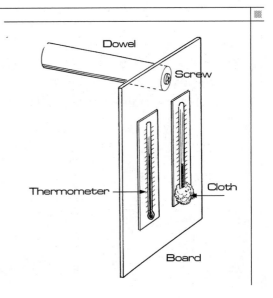

1. Glue the thermometers on the
   board (see illustration).

2. Place the cloth around one
   thermometer bulb and secure it
   with a tiny rubber band.

3. Attach the dowel with the screw.

4. Measure the relative humidity by
   using the psychrometer and the
   chart provided on the following
   page. The chart is accurate for
   a barometric pressure of
   74.27 centimeters Hg and temperatures above –10°C.
   Between 77.5 and 71 centimeters Hg, the values will be less
   than the error of observation.

(continued)

RELATIVE HUMIDITY C° CHART

Air Temp. Dry °C	Difference Between Wet and Dry Temperature °C											
	1°	2°	3°	4°	5°	6°	7°	8°	9°	10°	11°	12°
0	81	64	46	29	13							
5	86	72	58	45	33	20	7					
10	88	77	66	55	44	34	24	15	6			
15	90	80	71	61	53	44	36	27	20	13	6	
20	91	83	74	66	59	51	44	37	31	24	18	12
25	92	84	77	70	63	57	50	44	39	33	28	22
30	93	86	79	73	67	61	55	50	44	39	35	28
35	94	87	81	75	69	64	59	54	49	44	40	36
40	94	88	82	77	72	67	62	57	53	48	44	40

Relative Humidity %

Special Safety Consideration: This demonstration calls for thermometers, which may contain mercury. Be aware of safe disposal procedures for mercury should a thermometer break or leak.

Water vapor condenses back into a liquid when the temperature drops. The point of transition from a gas to a liquid is the **dew point.** As the temperature drops, air becomes saturated with water vapor, because cold air can hold less vapor than warm air. The fine water condensation that first appears is dew. Water freezes at 0°C or 32°F. When the humidity in the air is low, the dew point drops below the freezing temperature of water. If the air temperature drops to the dew point, then the water vapor in the air will change into frost (ice), not water.

Materials: thermometer, metal can, water, ice

- Half-fill the can with water. Place the thermometer in the can. Add ice cubes and stir gently. When condensation appears on the outside of the can, read the thermometer. This is the dew point for your room's air at this time.

Special Safety Consideration: This demonstration calls for a thermometer, which may contain mercury. Be aware of safe disposal procedures for mercury should a thermometer break or leak.

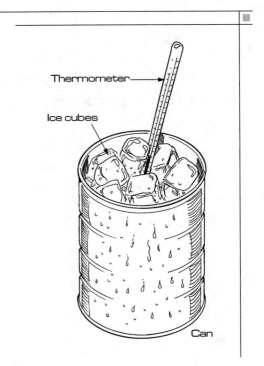

Thermometer

Ice cubes

Can

A **hygrometer** measures humidity in the air.

Materials: stand with clamp, glass rod or tubing, long human hair, small washer or button, toothpick (pointed), glue, index card, cardboard, masking tape

- Attach a small washer or button to the end of a washed human hair. Hang the hair from the glass rod and fasten it to the stand with some masking tape. The length of the hair will vary with humidity, and the little weight will move up and down. Glue a toothpick to the flat side of the washer. Place an index card on a support made from cardboard, behind the toothpick, and slowly calibrate the hygrometer according to daily weather forecasts.

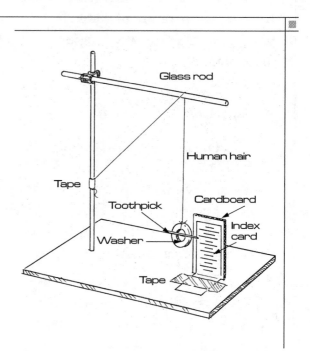

Glass rod

Human hair

Tape

Toothpick

Cardboard

Washer

Index card

Tape

Clouds form when air pressures drop, causing the temperature to drop. Water vapor begins to condense. For water vapor to condense, tiny particles, called **condensation nuclei**, must be present. These particles—such as dust, smoke, or salt—become the center of droplets that form a cloud.

Materials: pressure flask, stopper with two holes, small glass tube, rubber hose, hose clamp, steel valve stem from car or bicycle tire, tire pump, water, matches, sheet of black paper, flashlight, graduated cylinder, water, dry ice (optional)

- Prepare the stopper by inserting the tire valve stem through one hole and a small piece of glass tubing through the other one. On the outside end of the glass tubing, place a small piece of rubber hose and clamp it. Pour 25 mL of water in the flask. Light a match, and place it inside the bottle for a few seconds so that some smoke remains inside. Cover the bottle, and pump air into it to increase its internal pressure. Behind the bottle, place a large sheet of black paper and shine a light through the bottle. Open the clamp and let the air pressure inside the bottle drop. The temperature inside the bottle will drop. You will observe a cloud in the bottle. The smoke particles acted as condensation nuclei. (Optional: If you pack dry ice around the flask, some of the cloud will precipitate as snow.)

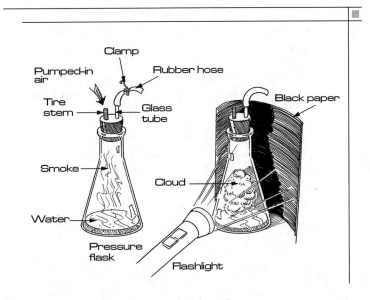

Special Safety Consideration: Do not allow students to handle dry ice. Handle dry ice only wearing gloves, and dispose of it safely.

Tornadoes form when warm, moist air masses meet with cold air. Light and moist air rises up while the cold air moves down. The path of the warm air is like a funnel, spiraling upwards and spinning around. As tornadoes move along the land, their spinning centers, being regions of very low pressure, suck up anything on the ground, with devastating effects.

Materials: two plastic 1-liter (or 2-liter) soda bottles, two hose washers, tornado device, water

- Place a hose washer on both ends of the plastic "tornado tube" connector before screwing on the bottles. Fill one bottle with water. Insert the tornado device between the two empty plastic soda bottles. Invert the assembly so that the water is in the upper bottle. Swirl the assembly clockwise several times. The liquid will assume the shape of a tornado.

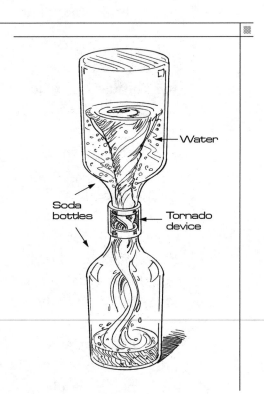

Water

Soda bottles

Tornado device

Note: You can buy a "tornado tube" for a few dollars from most scientific supply houses. Edmund Scientifics (800-728-6999/ www.scientificsonline.com) is a resource.

If you wish a larger demonstration device for a tornado than the one in Demonstration 57, build the following assembly.

Note: Exact measurements are not given in the materials list so that you can make the demonstrator box any size.

Materials: three glass panes (sides), board (side), black matte paint, glue, two square boards (base and cover), drill, high-intensity light, hot plate, flat pan, water

- Refer to the illustrations and follow these steps:

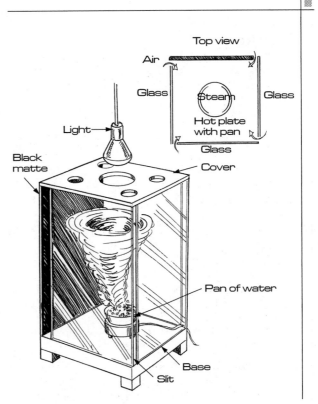

  1. Paint the nonglass box side a flat black. Secure the four sides to the wooden base, allowing half-inch slits as shown in the illustration. The painted surface should face inwards.

  2. Drill a large hole in the center of the cover for a high-intensity light to shine in. Drill at least four smaller holes to allow water vapor to escape.

  3. Place a hot plate on the base with a pan of water.

  4. To simulate a tornado, boil the water. Ambient air will enter through the side slits and create a whirlpool effect. Shine a high-intensity light through the cover hole to illuminate the demonstration.

Special Safety Consideration: This demonstration requires the use of potentially hazardous tools. Do not allow students to use sharp or electrical tools.

Earth is very massive, so it has a great deal of gravitational pull. The sun is much larger, and thus has even more gravity—enough to keep the planets in orbit. When the astronauts go up in the Space Shuttle, they aren't that far from Earth—only about 400 km, much closer than the moon. The moon certainly is held in Earth's gravitational force. Yet the astronauts on the space shuttle feel as if there is no gravity at all. Why is this?

The astronauts, and the shuttle itself, appear to float weightlessly because they are falling. Objects in orbit, like the shuttle and all of the satellites, are moving forward faster than they are falling, so they fall in an orbit around Earth. Things that are falling do not have weight.

In this experiment, you will see the effects of **freefall** on a couple of everyday objects.

Materials: two clothespins (spring variety), a large rubber band

Procedure:

1. Clip your clothespins onto opposite sides of a large rubber band.

2. Hold up one of the clothespins. Note that the weight of the other has changed the shape of the rubber band, stretching it out into an oval or ellipse.

3. Let go of the clothespin and let the assembly fall to the floor.

4. Note that the shape of the rubber band reverts to its original shape during the fall.

Conclusion: Why does the shape go back to its pre-weighted condition? What does freefall have to do with this situation?

The telescope was invented by a Dutch optician in 1608. Galileo Galilei was the first person to make a large model. With this telescope, he observed the moon and the planets in the solar system. Galileo built a **refracting telescope,** one that uses two convex lenses. A convex lens is thicker in the middle than at the edge, like a drop of water.

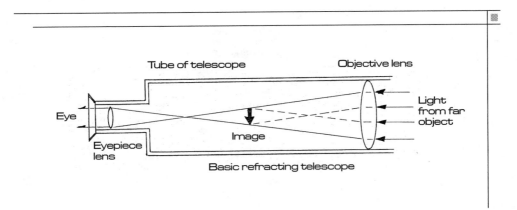

Basic refracting telescope

Materials: two magnifying glasses

- Take one magnifying lens and observe an object in the distance. Move the lens closer or farther away until you have a sharp image. The image will be inverted and smaller. Take the second magnifying glass and place it in front of your eye. Move this lens back and forth slowly until you see the object clearly. The object will appear larger.

Special Safety Consideration: Do not look at the sun with any telescope.

Mirror telescopes (reflecting telescopes) offer several advantages over refracting telescopes. They are smaller and gather more light. Isaac Newton built the first reflecting telescope in 1671. Each type of telescope has its own advantages.

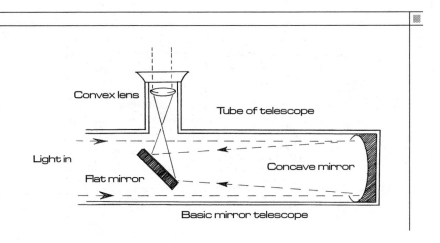

Basic mirror telescope

Materials: lightbulb in lamp base, magnifying lens, mirror with concave surface (magnifying mirror with two sides, used for makeup and shaving)

- Place the light on a table in a darkened room. Use the concave surface of the mirror to reflect the lightbulb on the wall. By moving the mirror slightly, try to get a sharp image on the wall. Observe the image of the bulb on the wall through the magnifying glass. By moving the magnifying glass around, you can make the bulb appear bigger.

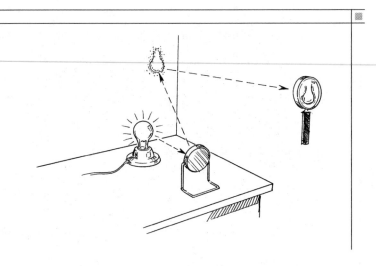

White light, such as from the sun, is the sum of all the colors of the rainbow. A rainbow appears when drops of water in the atmosphere break the light of the sun into its basic colors. A thick glass **prism** or a **diffraction grating** does the same thing. A diffraction grating is a thin plastic sheet that has thousands of fine lines ruled into it. These lines break up light like the water droplets that cause rainbows. When an element's flame is viewed through a **spectrometer** (or spectroscope), it shows a **spectrum,** or band of light, that is unique to that element. In this manner, substances can be identified accurately. By combining a spectroscope with a telescope, a scientist can find out the composition, size, direction of travel, and age of a star.

Materials: cardboard tube, diffraction grating, piece of black paper, tape, rubber band, razor blade, bright incandescent and bright fluorescent lights

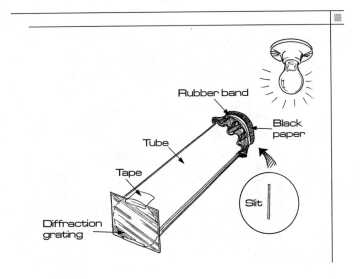

- Tape the diffraction grating on one end of the tube. Using a rubber band, cover the other end with the black paper. Cut a very fine slit through the center two-thirds of the paper. Point the slit toward a bright incandescent light and slowly rotate the tube until you see the spectrum. The spectra will appear to be on either side of the slit. Now try it with a fluorescent lamp. What differences do you notice?

Special Safety Consideration: Do not use this spectrometer, or any other, to look directly at the sun. Also, do not allow students to use the razor blade.

Astrolabes are ancient astronomical instruments used for measuring the **altitude** of particular stars. This was important to astronomers, of course, but also to sailors of ancient times who used the stars for navigation.

In this experiment, you will construct an astrolabe and use it to measure the heights of various objects in your schoolyard or around your home. Then, you will try to calculate the height of a particular star that the ancients used routinely for navigation.

Materials: scissors, astrolabe outline, poster board or manila file folder, glue or tape, string (17.8 cm or 7 inches), paper clip, star map

Making the Astrolabe:

1. Using scissors, cut out the astrolabe outline on the next page. Tape the outline onto a sheet of poster board or a manila folder, and cut carefully around the whole figure.

2. Make a tiny hole at the index point, marked with an *x*. Push the string through the hole, and tape the very end to the back of the cardboard. Attach a paper clip to serve as a weight at the other end of the string that will fall over the degree markings on the front of the astrolabe.

3. Fold the cardboard along the dashed lines so that the sides with the triangular notches form a right angle with the face of the astrolabe.

Using the Astrolabe:

1. Take the astrolabe outdoors. Find an object of some height— for instance, a tall tree—and sight the very top of the tree through both notches. Make sure that the paper clip and the string are hanging straight down—that is, the astrolabe must be perpendicular to the ground.

(continued)

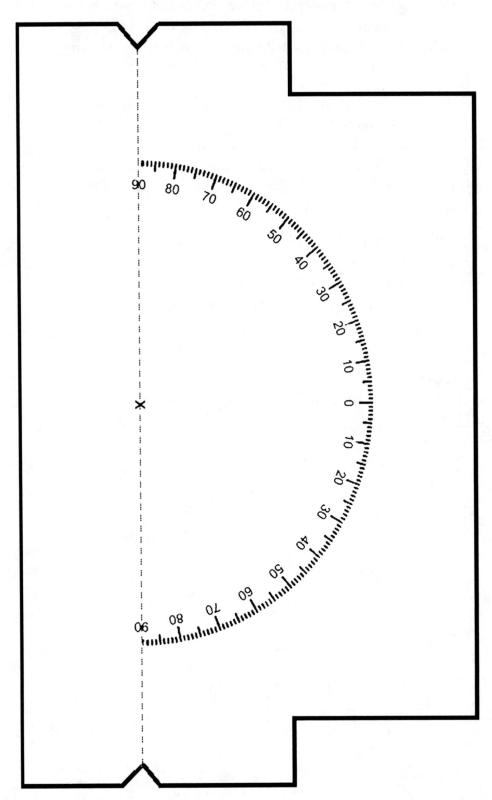

(continued)

2. Once you have the object well sighted, hold the string against the astrolabe, and only then move it from your eye. Record the height of the tall object in degrees. Try it with other objects.

3. At night, take the astrolabe home. Using a star map, locate the Big Dipper in the constellation Ursa Major. Using the "cup" of the big dipper, use the two pointer stars in the part of the cup farthest away from the handle and follow the line they make. Polaris, or the North Star, can be easily found this way.

4. When you can see Polaris through both notches, press the string to the cardboard and record the angle at which the string crosses the scale. This is the altitude of Polaris (its angle above the horizon) and is also your latitude on the globe.

Conclusion: How did ancient sailors use this method to determine their **latitude?** Could an astrolabe be used to figure **longitude?** Why or why not?

The brightness of a star is the light given off by its hot gases. **Apparent magnitude** is a measure of a star's apparent brightness, or luminosity, as viewed from Earth. If two stars of the same size and brightness are located so that one is near and the other far away, the closer one will appear brighter and have a greater apparent magnitude. There is also a different sort of measurement called absolute magnitude, which is the intrinsic luminosity of a celestial body (as a star) if viewed from a distance of 10 parsecs. Less bright does not mean necessarily less massive. Imagine a car moving toward you at night. Its headlights are dim at a great distance but are very bright as the car passes you.

Stars come in various sizes. Hot, blue stars are the most massive; yellow stars, such as our sun, are medium sized and of medium temperature; and red stars, during the main sequence, or normal life span, of the star, are cool and small. The length of time a star remains in its main sequence depends upon the mass of the star. Massive stars, such as blue giants, burn up their hydrogen fuel rapidly, and they may continue in this phase for only tens of thousands of years. Yellow stars live for billions of years. Scientists believe that red dwarfs have the potential for living trillions of years. At the end of a star's life, each star goes through a period during which it becomes larger than it was, and of a deep reddish color. This temporary phase is called the red giant phase.

The combination of spectroscopy and **radioastronomy** (wave analysis) are the principal tools used by modern astronomers to gain information about stars. Also, through observations made in deep space by a host of robotics devices, including earth-orbiting telescopes, data is gathered for visible light, X rays, infrared rays, ultraviolet rays, and other energy forms.

Materials: variac or light dimmer, lightbulb, lightbulb base, Bunsen burner, forceps, sewing needle, two light bases with two bulbs of different wattage

(continued)

- Set up the variac to provide power for the bulb base. By turning the variac control, you can make the bulb glow brighter and dimmer. A dim bulb is not nearly as hot as a bright one.

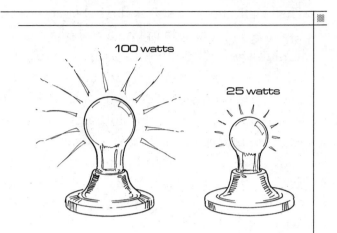

100 watts

25 watts

- Heat the sewing needle, and have students observe how it gets brighter as it gets hotter.

- Show students two lightbulbs of different wattage. The bulb with more watts is larger. The same is true for stars; at the same distance, the star with greater brightness is larger than a star with less brightness.

J. Weston Walch, Publisher

Easy Science Demos & Labs:
Earth Science

Parallax is the relative repositioning of an object seen against a fixed background when it is viewed from two different but equally distant points. Astronomers use parallax to find distances to the nearer stars. Parallax explains why sometimes people take photographs with heads partially cut off. The camera sees the person through the lens, while the photographer sees the person through a separate viewfinder. This is one of the reasons why single lens reflex cameras are so popular. These cameras view through the photographic lens and introduce no parallax error.

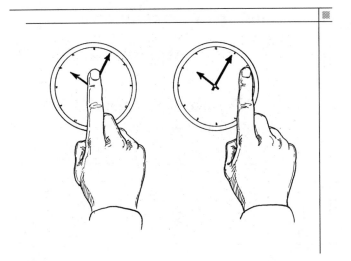

- Ask your students to look at an object (picture, clock, and so forth) across the room with both eyes open. Have them hold a finger away from their bodies in front of a specific point on this object. Have them close the left eye first, then open it and close the right eye. As they do so, the finger will appear to move to a different place for one eye as compared with the other one. This apparent motion is parallax. Have them find the finger's apparent position with both eyes open. The finger will appear closer to the view from the dominant eye.

Do you ever wonder how scientists can tell, with such accuracy, how large a celestial body is, even though it is very far away and may be so hot no one could possibly get near it? Today, you will be creating a pinhole viewer and, using information you already know, calculating to determine the diameter of the sun and of the moon.

Materials: sheet of cardboard, sheet of white paper, piece of aluminum foil (3 × 3 cm), map tack, tape, scissors, ruler, candle

Building the Pinhole Viewer:

1. Cut a square (2 × 2 cm) in the center of the sheet of cardboard.

2. Place the piece of aluminum foil over the opening, and tape it in place at the edges.

3. Using the map tack, puncture the foil to produce a small hole.

Determining the Size of the Sun:

1. Hold the pinhole viewer so that the light from the sun passes through the hole and falls on a sheet of white paper. Try to make the distance between the pinhole viewer and the paper as large as possible, and make sure you measure the distance from the viewer to the paper accurately.

2. Measure the diameter of the image of the sun on the paper.

3. You can calculate the diameter of the sun using the following formula:

Diameter of Image/Distance from Pinhole to Paper × Distance from Earth to Sun (149,600,000 km) = Diameter of Sun

(continued)

Determining the Size of the Moon:

You can use the same procedure to measure the diameter of the moon. Choose a night with a full moon. The distance between Earth and the moon is 384,000 km.

Conclusion: How much larger than the moon is the sun? If the sun is so much larger, why doesn't it appear to be larger in the sky?

Safety Warning: Try not to look directly at the sun.

The measurement of distance in space involves enormous numbers. To better describe great distances within our own solar system, astronomers use the distance from Earth to the sun, about 93 million miles (150 million kilometers), as 1 AU **(astronomical unit).**

Materials: several rolls of adding machine tape, metersticks, adhesive tape

- Ask student teams to model the relative distances of the planets from the sun by marking off the astronomical units for each planet on adding machine tape. Use one meter to represent each AU. Have students step outside the classroom and stretch out the tapes.

Planet	(AU)	Planet	(AU)	Planet	(AU)
Mercury	0.39	Mars	1.52	Uranus	19.2
Venus	0.72	Jupiter	5.2	Neptune	30.1
Earth	1	Saturn	9.5	Pluto	39.5

- An alternate activity is to measure the distances in astronomical units out on the playground or ball field. Have individual students act as markers by standing at each planetary position. Select an object to represent the position of the sun.

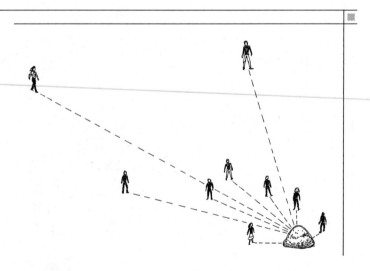

The **light-year** is an astronomical measure used to express distances to the stars. The light of the sun takes $8\frac{1}{3}$ minutes to reach us. A light-year is the distance that light travels in one year: 9.46 trillion kilometers (5.88 trillion miles). Light travels at 299,792.4562 kilometers (186,282 miles) per second, ± 1.1 meters per second. For ordinary calculations, this is rounded off to 300,000 kilometers per second, and that is the actual S.I. definition of light speed.

Materials: calculator

- Have your students calculate the distance that light travels in one year. The chart is for your reference.

Time	Seconds	Travel Distance of Light (kilometers)
1 second	1	300,000
1 minute	60	18,000,000
1 hour	3,600	1,080,000,000
1 day	86,400	25,920,000,000
1 week	604,800	181,440,000,000
1 year	220,900,000	9,460,800,000,000

The sun sends out enormous amounts of energy. Earth receives about $^{1}/_{2,000,000,000}$ (one two-billionth) of the sun's energy, despite the filtering out by our atmosphere. Sunshine contains invisible **ultraviolet (UV)** rays that can burn the skin and cause cancer. To prevent this, one needs to use sunscreen. Ultraviolet rays are radiation with a wavelength slightly longer than X rays.

Materials: salad oil, sunscreen, two sheets of colored paper (different colors)

- Cover one half of a sheet of colored paper with salad oil, the other half with sunscreen. Expose the paper to the sun for one morning. Repeat with another color. The sunscreen will prevent the fading of the color. Keep a sheet of each paper, away from light, for later comparison.

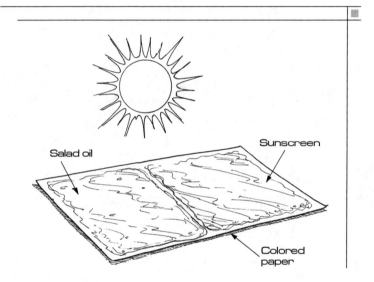

Salad oil

Sunscreen

Colored paper

Viewing the sun's activity is desirable at times, especially during solar eclipses. Quality telescopes are equipped with solar viewing plates and solar filters. You need to check, if you buy a filter, that it has the UL (United Laboratories) seal of approval. Many inexpensive filters heat up and break during observations, with subsequent damage to the viewer's eyes. Looking directly at the sun will damage the eyes. Looking at the sun through several layers of exposed photographic film is also harmful, because infrared rays (heat) will go through to cause severe and permanent eye damage. The pinhole projector described here provides a safe way to observe the sun and solar eclipses.

Materials: shoe box, index card, needle, adhesive tape

- Remove the cover of the shoe box. With the needle, punch a small hole near the middle of one end of the box. Tape an index card inside the box at the opposite end of the hole. Point the hole toward the sun and move the box until an image of the sun appears on the index card.

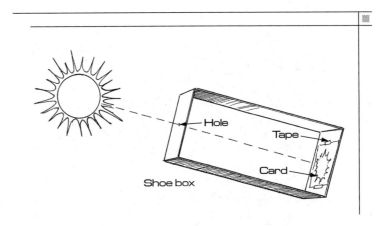

Special Safety Consideration: Never look, or allow students to look, directly at the sun.

A solar eclipse occurs when the moon, in its rotation around Earth, is in a position between the sun and Earth, thus blocking some of the sun's rays. If only part of the sun's face is blocked, it is a partial eclipse. If the whole face of the sun is obscured, then it is a total eclipse. The darkest shadow cast by the moon is the **umbra,** while the lighter one is the **penumbra.**

Materials: globe, flashlight or slide/filmstrip projector, orange or tennis ball

- Darken your classroom. Have one of your students stand a foot or two from the wall. Shine a light at the student, and have the class notice the shadow of the student projected on the wall. The shadow goes from light edges (penumbra) to dark center (umbra).

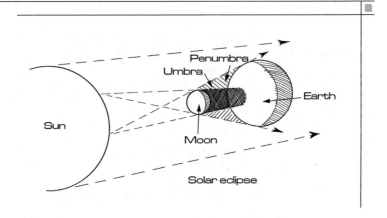

- Darken your classroom. Shine the light source (sun) from five feet away onto the globe (Earth). Place the orange (moon) between the sun and Earth. Have your students look at the globe from a position behind the light source. A shadow will appear on the globe.

- Place the observers behind the globe and block all the light with the orange. This will simulate a total eclipse.

A lunar eclipse occurs when Earth comes between the sun and the moon. The moon darkens as it moves into Earth's shadow. The darkest Earth shadow is the umbra and the lighter one, the penumbra.

Materials: globe, flashlight or slide/filmstrip projector, orange or tennis ball

- Darken your classroom. Shine the light source (sun) from five feet away onto the globe (Earth). Place the orange (moon) in the shadow

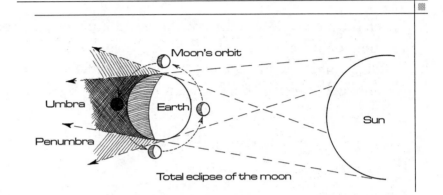

behind the globe. Have your students look at the orange from a position beside the globe. They will observe that the orange is in the globe's shadow.

You have probably noticed that, when the moon is low, just above the horizon, it looks very large, and when it is higher in the sky, it seems much smaller. There are also color differences. When the moon is at the horizon, it is reddish or yellowish, and when high in the sky, it seems whiter.

Why does the color change? The change is a result of atmospheric conditions near the horizon, not unlike the causes of colors we see at sunrise or sunset. The size change, however, is an optical illusion.

When the moon is low in the sky, our brains automatically compare it to things on the ground that we already know are big, like trees and buildings. Since the moon looks bigger than those already-big things, we think it's especially huge when it is closer to the horizon.

Materials: stiff cardboard, pencil or pen

Procedure:

1. When the moon is low, just above the horizon, hold the card at arm's length and mark the diameter of the moon on the card.

2. Look at the moon again a few hours later. Hold up your card and compare the lines. Is the moon smaller than before?

Conclusion: What did you notice about the actual lunar size from horizon to **zenith?** Can you think of other optical illusions that are caused by the brain's attempt to reconcile information?

The word *inertia* means "laziness" in Latin. Newton's first law states that objects at rest want to stay at rest, and objects in motion want to continue to move in the same direction until another force acts on them. Inertia is this resistence to changes in motion. Objects in motion usually slow down only because friction or other combined forces oppose their motion. Planets stay in orbit, and stellar mechanics are orderly, due to the law of inertia.

Materials: index card, coin, broom, large jar (plastic, if possible), some cloth, billiard ball, pie tin, plastic cup, table

- Balance an index card horizontally on one of your fingers. Place a coin on top of it. Remove the card by flicking its edge with your finger. Practice this until the coin remains on your finger.

- Place a billiard ball on top of an inverted cup, sitting in the middle of a pie tin, on top of a jar. Center the entire assembly. Then place it near the edge of a table, so that the jar is near the table's edge while the pie tin goes beyond the table's edge. Hold the broom vertically so that it touches the table's edge. Step on the bottom of the broom. Pull the handle away from the table, and let go. With practice, the broom will hit the pie tin (the table's edge will stop the travel of the broom), and the ball will fall into the jar.

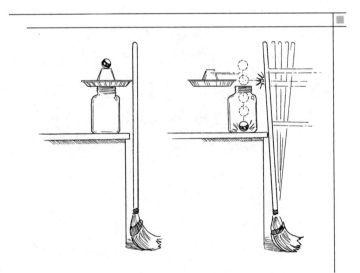

Special Safety Consideration: If you are using a glass jar, place cloths or paper inside the jar to prevent breakage.

The force of **gravity** pulls all objects down to Earth. If you throw an object, it goes forward and down. Earth is not the only object that pulls with the force of gravity. All stars and planets in the universe have gravity. The force of gravitational attraction keeps planets in orbit around the stars.

Materials: piece of string, roll of masking tape

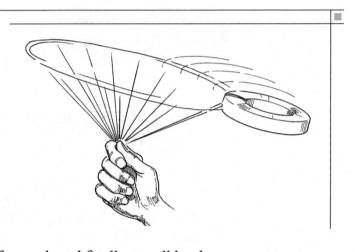

- Drop any object. The fall demonstrates Earth's gravity.

- Tie the roll of tape to the end of the string and start spinning it around. It will go in a circular path. The string represents the invisible force of gravity that keeps planets in orbit. If you let go, it will continue going forward, and finally, it will land on the floor. This shows the gravitational pull of Earth on the roll of tape.

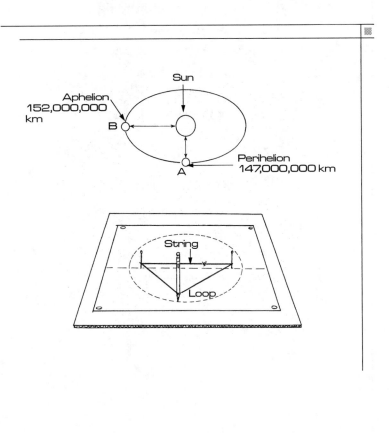

Earth and the other planets travel in elliptical orbits around the sun.
Ellipses are ovals. **Aphelion** is the point at which a planet is farthest
(*B*) from the sun. **Perihelion** is the point at which a planet is closest
to the sun (*A*). A planet's motion around the sun is a **revolution**.
Earth's revolution takes a year to complete.

Materials: string, two push pins, pencil, sheet of paper, sheet of
cardboard

- Cut a piece of string
  about 30 centimeters
  long. Tie the ends
  together to make a
  loop. Place the paper
  on top of the
  cardboard. Draw a
  centerline parallel to
  the longer side of the
  sheet of paper. Stick
  the two pins into
  the centerline,
  approximately one
  third of the way
  from each end of
  the paper. While
  someone holds the
  pins, place the string
  loop over the pins,
  and draw an ellipse
  by keeping the pencil
  taut inside the string loop.

Earth turns on its axis once a day. The side of the planet facing the sun has daylight, while the opposite side has night. This motion of Earth is **rotation.** Earth rotates on an axis that is 23.5° off from the vertical. This tilt accounts for the difference between summer and winter, in the length of the days and nights.

Materials: globe, flashlight

- Darken the room. Shine the light on one side of the globe from about five feet away. Have the students observe from one of the sides of the globe. Gently turn the globe from west to east to simulate Earth's rotation.

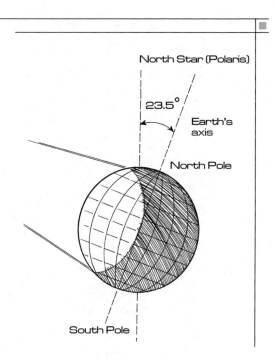

North Star (Polaris)

23.5°

Earth's axis

North Pole

South Pole

The polar regions are colder than the equatorial regions because, at the poles, the rays of the sun strike Earth at a slant. At the equator, the rays of the sun shine nearly perpendicular to Earth's surface. Perpendicular rays strike with more energy, because the energy is concentrated over a smaller surface area. At the poles, the same energy is distributed over a larger area. Therefore, very little energy is available per square unit as compared to the equator.

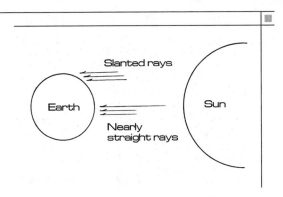

Materials: flashlight (or slide/filmstrip projector)

- Darken the classroom, and aim the flashlight at the ceiling. First show the small area lit up by a beam perpendicular to the ceiling. Start slanting the light until the beam covers a large ceiling area. If you have ceiling tiles, count them at the start and at the end. Point out to your students that you have not changed the light source; therefore, there must be less light energy per square area illuminated, since the same light is spread over a larger area. The same is true for the sun's rays hitting different parts of Earth.

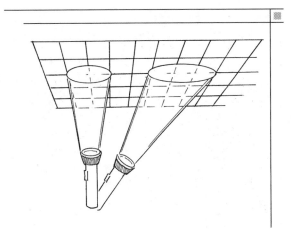

95

Prerequisite: Demonstration 74: The Poles Are Colder Than the Equator.

Seasons change due to Earth's rotation around the sun. Since Earth is slanted by 23.5° off the vertical, the Northern Hemisphere receives straight rays of the sun for six months, while the Southern Hemisphere receives slanted rays. At this time, it is summer in the Northern Hemisphere and winter in the Southern. During the next six months, the situation is reversed.

Materials: two plastic glasses or cups, orange or other spherical object, felt pen, two toothpicks, masking tape, flashlight or other light source

- Do the following steps in order:

1. Prepare the orange by sticking the two toothpicks into its opposite sides. Allow about two inches of each toothpick to stick out, to represent the earth's axis. Mark a great circle on the orange, to mark its equator. Place the orange on a glass with the axis offset from perpendicular (straight up and down) by about 20° to 30°.

2. Using a table or the floor, place the flashlight horizontally on a glass and tape it down to prevent its rolling off.

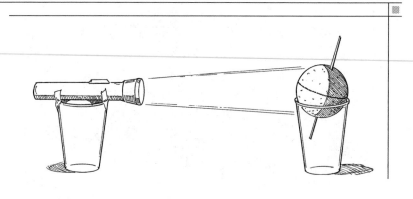

Turn on the flashlight. Place the model of Earth (the orange on the glass) 30 to 40 inches from the flashlight. Make certain that its axis is pointing away from the light. Have students notice that the Southern Hemisphere receives light that is almost perpendicular, while the Northern Hemisphere

(continued)

receives light that is slanted. This shows winter in the Northern Hemisphere, where there is less solar energy per square meter or yard. It is summer in the Southern Hemisphere.

3. Move the cup 90° around the light, but be careful not to turn the cup, so its axis will remain pointed in the same direction as in step 2. Maintain the same distance. Turn on the flashlight pointing toward the orange, and notice that the light equally covers both hemispheres. This is true because neither hemisphere is slanted at this point. This represents conditions in spring or fall.

4. Again move the cup 90°. Be careful not to change the direction of the axis. Turn the light on the orange. Now the Northern Hemisphere receives light that is almost perpendicular, while the Southern Hemisphere receives light at a slant. It is summer in the Northern Hemisphere and winter in the South. The next 90° position will again be fall and spring.

5. Point out that the Northern Hemisphere has winter when Earth is closer to the sun in its elliptical orbit. Therefore, it is not the distance, but the tilt of Earth to the sun, that determines the seasons.

There is an **equinox,** an "equal night," two times every year, and there are two **solstices,** times when day or night is at its peak. The equinoxes occur on the first day of spring and the first day of autumn, while the solstices happen on the first day of summer and the first day of winter. It is pretty easy to see that sunrise isn't always in the same place or at the same time of day. At 6 P.M. in July, the sun is still shining brightly, while at 6 P.M. in January, the sky is completely dark.

With this experiment, you can verify that the sun appears to be in a different location in the sky at a specific time each day—with just one exception. On the vernal (spring) equinox and the autumnal equinox, the sun appears to be in the exact same position in the sky.

Materials: 60- × 60-cm cardboard square, 30-cm wooden stick with diameter of 6–12 mm, glue, marker

Procedure:

1. Glue the wooden stick upright to the cardboard square, halfway along one side of the cardboard.

2. Place the cardboard square on a flat surface where it will be exposed to the sun. Orient the cardboard so that the stick side is facing the sun. Do not move it for the life of this experiment. Take a reading at the same time each day.

3. The sun will create a shadow on the board. Using the marker, mark the place on the board where the shadow ends, and write down the date.

4. Repeat this daily or weekly.

5. At the end of a year, you will have a complete pattern of the precession of the equinoxes, but long before that, you will start to see a definite pattern.

Conclusion: Describe or predict any days when the shadow will appear in the exact same position at the same time. Suggest a place, somewhere on the planet, where the shadow will fall in the same spot every day. Explain why you think this is so.

Appendix

1. Assessing Laboratory Reports

This book contains 10 student laboratory assignments for which students should be expected to produce written reports. Go over what you want to see in a lab report with your students before they start. Information should include:

- **Purpose:** Why is this lab being performed? What is the objective of the lab?

- **Hypothesis:** Given the initial level of knowledge, what do students expect for an outcome and why?

- **Materials list:** Students should be told that one of the main reasons for writing lab reports is so that the labs can be replicated by others. A well-organized materials list makes it easier for the reader to understand the lab, and makes redoing the experiment much easier as well.

- **Procedure:** Likewise, a student should include each step of the procedure that the lab partners or group actually followed.

- **Data:** What events or measurements were observed in the lab?

- **Conclusion:** What were the results? What were the limitations? Did their hypothesis match the data? If something went wrong, what does the student think happened?

(continued)

© 1997, 2003
J. Weston Walch, Publisher

*Easy Science Demos & Labs:
Earth Science*

1. Assessing Laboratory Reports *(continued)*

In order to give you a quick guide to assessing lab reports, we have constructed the following rubric:

	1	**2**	**3**	**4**
Understanding of Concept	Poor	Adequate	Good	Outstanding
Methodology	Poor	Adequate	Good	Outstanding
Organization of Experiment	Poor	Adequate	Good	Outstanding
Organization of Report	Poor	Adequate	Good	Outstanding

Laboratory reports are an important stepping stone for young scientists, but can become burdensome to correct. We hope this rubric assists the typical busy teacher in providing a quality lab experience without sacrificing the deeper knowledge of the scientific method that writing lab reports reinforces among young scientists.

Easy Science Demos & Labs:
Earth Science

2. Astronomical Data #1

	Units	Sun	Mercury	Venus	Earth	Moon	Mars	Jupiter	Saturn	Uranus	Neptune	Pluto
Average distance from the sun	Miles (in millions)	25 trillion to nearest star	36	67.2	92.9	238,900 from Earth	141.6	483.3	886.7	1,782	2,794	5,900
Average distance from the sun	Kilometers (in millions)	41 trillion to nearest star	57.9	108.1	149.5	384,500 from Earth	227.8	778.3	1,427	2,869	4,497	5,900
Average distance from the sun	Astronom‑ical units	4.3 light–years to nearest star	0.387	0.723	1.00	0.0026 from Earth	1.524	5.203	9.539	19.18	30.06	39.44
Length of year (sidereal)	Period of orbit	246 million years to orbit galaxy	88.0 days	224.7 days	365.26 days	27.32 days to orbit Earth	1.88 years	11.86 years	29.46 years	84.01 years	164.8 years	247.7 years
Length of day	Period of rotation	25d8h24m equatorial	58d16h2m	243d0h14m retrograde	23h56m4s	27d7h43m	24h37m12s	9h48m48s equatorial	10h39m24s equatorial	15h36m? retrograde	18h30m?	6d9h23m
Orbital speed average	Miles per hour average	560,000 around galactic ctr.	107,300	78,500	66,800	2,300	54,100	29,300	21,600	15,300	12,200	10,600
Orbital speed average	Kilometers per hour average	90,000 around galactic ctr.	172,700	126,300	107,400	5,700	87,000	47,200	34,800	24,500	19,600	17,100
Equatorial diameter	Miles	865,000	3,031	7,521	7,927	2,160	4,197	88,733	74,600	31,600	30,200	1,900?
Equatorial diameter	Kilometers	1,392,000	4,878	12,104	12,756	3,476	6,794	142,796	120,000	50,800	48,600	3,000?
Equatorial diameter	Earth = 1	109	0.382	0.949	1.00	0.2725	0.5326	11.19	9.41	3.98	3.81	0.24?
Mass	Earth = 1	332,946	0.055	0.815	1.00	0.012	0.107	317.9	95.17	14.56	17.24	0.002?
Volume	Earth = 1	1,300,000	0.056	0.855	1.00	0.020	0.151	1,403	833	63.0	55.3	0.013?
Density mean	g/cm³ Water = 1	1.41	5.44	5.24	5.52	3.36	3.93	1.33	0.70	1.28	1.75	0.69?
Gravity on surface	Earth = 1	27.8	0.38	0.90	1.00	0.16	0.38	2.87	1.32	0.93	1.23	0.03?

Legend: d = days   h = hours   m = minutes   s = seconds   ? = approximate

	Units	Sun	Mercury	Venus	Earth	Moon	Mars	Jupiter	Saturn	Uranus	Neptune	Pluto
Escape velocity	Miles per hour	1,378,000	9.619	23,042	25,055	5,324	11,185	141,828	88,139	48,096	54,136	751?
Escape velocity	Kilometers per second	616	4.3	10.3	11.2	2.3	5.0	63.4	39.4	21.5	24.2	0.34?
Temperature extremes	High core Fahrenheit	27,000,000 °F	660°F	896°F	136.4°F	225°F	80°F	53,500°F				−390°F
Temperature extremes	High core Celsius	15,000,000 °C	350°C	480°C	58°C	107°C	27°C	29,700°C				−234°C
Temperature extremes	Low core Fahrenheit	10,800°F	−270°F	−27°F†	−126.9°F	−243°F	−190°F	−140°F†	−292°F†	−346°F†	−364°F†	−140°F?
Temperature extremes	Low core Celsius	6,000°C	−170°C	−33°C†	−88.3°C	−153°C	−123°C	−95°C†	−180°C†	−210°C†	−220°C†	−230°C?
Number of known moons		9 Planets	0	0	1	—	2	16+ rings	23?+ rings	5+ rings	2	1
Eccentricity in orbit	Circular orbit = 0	—	0.206	0.007	0.017	0.055	0.093	0.048	0.056	0.047	0.009	0.250
Inclination of equator	To orbital plane of planets	7.25° Equator to ecliptic	<2°	183.4°	23.45°	6.7°	23.98°	3.1°	26.7°	97.9°	28.8°	90°?
Oblateness of planet		0	0	0	0.003	0.0005	0.009	0.063	0.109	0.063	0.026	?
Atmosphere	Principal gases	H_2, He	none	CO_2	N_2, O_2	none	CO_2	H_2, He	H_2, He	H_2, He	H_2, He	none

Legend: † = cloudtops   ? = approximate CO_2 = carbon dioxide N_2 = nitrogen H_2 = hydrogen   He = Helium

4. Moons in the Solar System

The moons are arranged in their order of closeness from the planets.

Earth	Mars	Jupiter	Saturn	Uranus	Neptune	Pluto
1. Moon	1. Phobos 2. Deimos	1. 1979–J3 2. Adrastea 3. Amalthea 4. 1972–J2 5. Io 6. Europa 7. Ganymede 8. Callisto 9. Leda 10. Himalia 11. Lysithea 12. Elara 13. Ananke 14. Carme 15. Pasiphae 16. Sinope	1. 1980–S28 2. 1980–S27 3. 1980–S26 4. 1980–S1 5. 1980–S3 6. Mimas 7. Enceladus 8. Tethys 9. Tethys B 10. Tethys C 11. Dione 12. Dione B 13. Rhea 14. Titan 15. Hyperion 16. Iapetus 17. Phoebe At least six more are suspected to be there.	1. Miranda 2. Ariel 3. Ubrial 4. Titania 5. Oberon	1. Triton 2. Nereid	1. Charon

© 1997, 2003
J. Weston Walch, Publisher

Easy Science Demos & Labs:
Earth Science

5. Density of Liquids

approx. gm/cm^3 at 20°C

Acetone	0.79
Alcohol (ethyl)	0.79
Alcohol (methyl)	0.81
Benzene	0.90
Carbon disulfide	1.29
Carbon tetrachloride	1.56
Chloroform	1.50
Ether	0.74
Gasoline	0.68
Glycerin	1.26
Kerosene	0.82
Linseed oil (boiled)	0.94
Mercury	13.6
Milk	1.03
Naphtha (petroleum)	0.67
Olive oil	0.92
Sulfuric acid	1.82
Turpentine	0.87
Water 0° C	0.99
Water 4° C	1.00
Water–sea	1.03

6. Altitude, Barometer, and Boiling Point

altitude (approx. ft)	barometer reading (cm of mercury)	boiling point (°C)
15,430	43.1	84.9
10,320	52.0	89.8
6,190	60.5	93.8
5,510	62.0	94.4
5,060	63.1	94.9
4,500	64.4	95.4
3,950	65.7	96.0
3,500	66.8	96.4
3,060	67.9	96.9
2,400	69.6	97.6
2,060	70.4	97.9
1,520	71.8	98.5
970	73.3	99.0
530	74.5	99.5
0	76.0	100.0
−550	77.5	100.5

7. Specific Gravity

gram/cm^3 at 20°C

Agate	2.5–2.6	Granite*	2.7	Polystyrene	1.06
Aluminum	2.7	Graphite	2.2	Quartz	2.6
Brass*	8.5	Human body–normal	1.07	Rock salt	2.1–2.2
Butter	0.86	Human body–lungs full	1.00	Rubber (gum)	0.92
Cellural cellulose acetate	0.75	Ice	0.92	Silver	10.5
Celluloid	1.4	Iron (cast)*	7.9	Steel	7.8
Cement*	2.8	Lead	11.3	Sulfur (roll)	2.0
Coal (anthracite)*	1.5	Limestone	2.7	Tin	7.3
Coal (bituminous)*	1.3	Magnesium	1.74	Tungsten	18.8
Copper	8.9	Marble*	2.7	Wood: Rock Elm	0.76
Cork	0.22–0.26	Nickel	8.8	Balsa	0.16
Diamond	3.1–3.5	Opal	2.1–2.3	Red Oak	0.67
German Silver	8.4	Osmium	22.5	Southern Pine	0.56
Glass (common)	2.5	Paraffin	0.9	White Pine	0.4
Gold	19.3	Platinum	21.4	Zinc	7.1

*Non–homogeneous material. Specific gravity may vary. Table gives average value.

8. Temperature Conversion (Celsius to Fahrenheit)

C°	F°	C°	F°	C°	F°	C°	F°	C°	F°	C°	F°
250	482.00	200	392.00	150	302.00	100	212.00	50	122.00	0	32.00
249	480.20	199	390.20	149	300.20	99	210.20	49	120.20	−1	30.20
248	478.40	198	388.40	148	298.40	98	208.40	48	118.40	−2	28.40
247	476.60	197	386.60	147	296.60	97	206.60	47	116.60	−3	26.60
246	474.80	196	384.80	146	294.80	96	204.80	46	114.80	−4	24.80
245	473.00	195	383.00	145	293.00	95	203.00	45	113.00	−5	23.00
244	471.20	194	381.20	144	291.20	94	201.20	44	111.20	−6	21.20
243	469.40	193	379.40	143	289.40	93	199.40	43	109.40	−7	19.40
242	467.60	192	377.60	142	287.60	92	197.60	42	107.60	−8	17.60
241	465.80	191	375.80	141	285.80	91	195.80	41	105.80	−9	15.80
240	464.00	190	374.00	140	284.00	90	194.00	40	104.00	−10	14.00
239	462.20	189	372.20	139	282.20	89	192.20	39	102.20	−11	12.20
238	460.40	188	370.40	138	280.40	88	190.40	38	100.40	−12	10.40
237	458.60	187	368.60	137	278.60	87	188.60	37	98.60	−13	8.60
236	456.80	186	366.80	136	276.80	86	186.80	36	96.80	−14	6.80
235	455.00	185	365.00	135	275.00	85	185.00	35	95.00	−15	5.00
234	453.20	184	363.20	134	273.20	84	183.20	34	93.20	−16	3.20
233	451.40	183	361.40	133	271.40	83	181.40	33	91.40	−17	1.40
232	449.60	182	359.60	132	269.60	82	179.60	32	89.60	−18	−0.40
231	447.80	181	357.80	131	267.80	81	177.80	31	87.80	−19	−2.20
230	446.00	180	356.00	130	266.00	80	176.00	30	86.00	−20	−4.00
229	444.20	179	354.20	129	264.20	79	174.20	29	84.20	−21	−5.80
228	442.40	178	352.40	128	262.40	78	172.40	28	82.40	−22	−7.60
227	440.60	177	350.60	127	260.60	77	170.60	27	80.60	−23	−9.40
226	438.80	176	348.80	126	258.80	76	168.80	26	78.80	−24	−11.20
225	437.00	175	347.00	125	257.00	75	167.00	25	77.00	−25	−13.00
224	435.20	174	345.20	124	255.20	74	165.20	24	75.20	−26	−14.80
223	433.40	173	343.40	123	253.40	73	163.40	23	73.40	−27	−16.60
222	431.60	172	341.60	122	251.60	72	161.60	22	71.60	−28	−18.40
221	429.80	171	339.80	121	249.80	71	159.80	21	69.80	−29	−20.20
220	428.00	170	338.00	120	248.00	70	158.00	20	68.00	−30	−22.00
219	426.20	169	336.20	119	246.20	69	156.20	19	66.20	−31	−23.80
218	424.40	168	334.40	118	244.40	68	154.40	18	64.40	−32	−25.60
217	422.60	167	332.60	117	242.60	67	152.60	17	62.60	−33	−27.40
216	420.80	166	330.80	116	240.80	66	150.80	16	60.80	−34	−29.20
215	419.00	165	329.00	115	239.00	65	149.00	15	59.00	−35	−31.00
214	417.20	164	327.20	114	237.20	64	147.20	14	57.20	−36	−32.80
213	415.40	163	325.40	113	235.40	63	145.40	13	55.40	−37	−34.60
212	413.60	162	323.60	112	233.60	62	143.60	12	53.60	−38	−36.40
211	411.80	161	321.80	111	231.80	61	141.80	11	51.80	−39	−38.20
210	410.00	160	320.00	110	230.00	60	140.00	10	50.00	−40	−40.00
209	408.20	159	318.20	109	228.20	59	138.20	9	48.20	−41	−41.80
208	406.40	158	316.40	108	226.40	58	136.40	8	46.40	−42	−43.60
207	404.60	157	314.60	107	224.60	57	134.60	7	44.60	−43	−45.40
206	402.80	156	312.80	106	222.80	56	132.80	6	42.80	−44	−47.20
205	401.00	155	311.00	105	221.00	55	131.00	5	41.00	−45	−49.00
204	399.20	154	309.20	104	219.20	54	129.20	4	39.20	−46	−50.80
203	397.40	153	307.40	103	217.40	53	127.40	3	37.40	−47	−52.60
202	395.60	152	305.60	102	215.60	52	125.60	2	35.60	−48	−54.40
201	393.80	151	303.80	101	213.80	51	123.80	1	33.80	−49	−56.20

9. Temperature Conversion (Fahrenheit to Celsius)

F°	C°	F°	C°	F°	C°	F°	C°	F°	C°	F°	C°
250	121.11	200	93.33	150	65.56	100	37.78	50	10.00	0	−17.78
249	120.56	199	92.78	149	65.00	99	37.22	49	9.44	−1	−18.33
248	120.00	198	92.22	148	64.44	98	36.67	48	8.89	−2	−18.89
247	119.44	197	91.67	147	63.89	97	36.11	47	8.33	−3	−19.44
246	118.89	196	91.11	146	63.33	96	35.56	46	7.78	−4	−20.00
245	118.33	195	90.56	145	62.78	95	35.00	45	7.22	−5	−20.55
244	117.78	194	90.00	144	62.22	94	34.44	44	6.67	−6	−21.11
243	117.22	193	89.44	143	61.67	93	33.89	43	6.11	−7	−21.67
242	116.67	192	88.89	142	61.11	92	33.33	42	5.56	−8	−22.22
241	116.11	191	88.33	141	60.56	91	32.78	41	5.00	−9	−22.78
240	115.56	190	87.78	140	60.00	90	32.22	40	4.44	−10	−23.33
239	115.00	189	87.22	139	59.44	89	31.67	39	3.89	−11	−23.89
238	114.44	188	86.67	138	58.89	88	31.11	38	3.33	−12	−24.44
237	113.89	187	86.11	137	58.33	87	30.56	37	2.78	−13	−25.00
236	113.33	186	85.56	136	57.78	86	30.00	36	2.22	−14	−25.56
235	112.78	185	85.00	135	57.22	85	29.44	35	1.67	−15	−26.11
234	112.22	184	84.44	134	56.67	84	28.89	34	1.11	−16	−26.67
233	111.67	183	83.89	133	56.11	83	28.33	33	0.56	−17	−27.22
232	111.11	182	83.33	132	55.56	82	27.78	32	0.00	−18	−27.78
231	110.56	181	82.78	131	55.00	81	27.22	31	−0.56	−19	−28.33
230	100.00	180	82.22	130	54.44	80	26.67	30	−1.11	−20	−28.89
229	109.44	179	81.67	129	53.89	79	26.11	29	−1.67	−21	−29.44
228	108.89	178	81.11	128	53.33	78	25.56	28	−2.22	−22	−30.00
227	108.33	177	80.56	127	52.78	77	25.00	27	−2.78	−23	−30.56
226	107.78	176	80.00	126	52.22	76	24.44	26	−3.33	−24	−31.11
225	107.22	175	79.44	125	51.67	75	23.89	25	−3.89	−25	−31.67
224	106.67	174	78.89	124	51.11	74	23.33	24	−4.44	−26	−32.22
223	106.11	173	78.33	123	50.56	73	22.78	23	−5.00	−27	−32.78
222	105.56	172	77.78	122	50.00	72	22.22	22	−5.56	−28	−33.33
221	105.00	171	77.22	121	49.44	71	21.67	21	−6.11	−29	−33.89
220	104.44	170	76.67	120	48.89	70	21.11	20	−6.67	−30	−34.44
219	103.89	169	76.11	119	48.33	69	20.56	19	−7.22	−31	−35.00
218	103.33	168	75.56	118	47.78	68	20.00	18	−7.78	−32	−35.56
217	102.78	167	75.00	117	47.22	67	19.44	17	−8.33	−33	−36.11
216	102.22	166	74.44	116	46.67	66	18.89	16	−8.89	−34	−36.67
215	101.67	165	73.89	115	46.11	65	18.33	15	−9.44	−35	−37.22
214	101.11	164	73.33	114	45.56	64	17.78	14	−10.00	−36	−37.78
213	100.56	163	72.78	113	45.00	63	17.22	13	−10.56	−37	−38.33
212	100.00	162	72.22	112	44.44	62	16.67	12	−11.11	−38	−38.89
211	99.44	161	71.67	111	43.89	61	16.11	11	−11.67	−39	−39.44
210	98.89	160	71.11	110	43.33	60	15.56	10	−12.22	−40	−40.00
209	98.33	159	70.56	109	42.78	59	15.00	9	−12.78	−41	−40.56
208	97.78	158	70.00	108	42.22	58	14.44	8	−13.33	−42	−41.11
207	97.22	157	69.44	107	41.67	57	13.89	7	−13.89	−43	−41.67
206	96.67	156	68.89	106	41.11	56	13.33	6	−14.44	−44	−42.22
205	96.11	155	68.33	105	40.56	55	12.78	5	−15.00	−45	−42.78
204	95.56	154	67.78	104	40.00	54	12.22	4	−15.56	−46	−43.33
203	95.00	153	67.22	103	39.44	53	11.67	3	−16.11	−47	−43.89
202	94.44	152	66.67	102	38.89	52	11.11	2	−16.67	−48	−44.44
201	93.89	151	66.11	101	38.33	51	10.56	1	−17.22	−49	−45.00

10. Units: Conversions and Constants

From	To	× By
Acres	Square feet	43,560
Acres	Square meters	4,046.8564
Acre-feet	Cubic feet	43,560
Avogadro's number	6.02252×10^{23}	
Barrel (US dry)	Barrel (US liquid)	0.96969
Barrel (US liquid)	Barrel (US dry)	1.03125
Bars	Atmospheres	0.98692
Bars	Grams/square centimeter	1,019.716
Cubic feet	Acre-feet	2.2956841×10^{-5}
Cubic feet	Cubic centimeters	28,316.847
Cubic feet	Cubic meters	0.028316984
Cubic feet	Gallons (US liquid)	7.4805195
Cubic feet	Quarts (US liquid)	29.922078
Cubic inches	Cubic centimeters	16.38706
Cubic inches	Cubic feet	0.0005787037
Cubic inches	Gallons (US liquid)	0.004329004
Cubic inches	Liters	0.016387064
Cubic inches	Ounces (US liquid)	0.5541125
Cubic inches	Quarts (US liquid)	0.03463203
Cubic meters	Acre-feet	0.0008107131
Cubic meters	Barrels (US liquid)	8.386414
Cubic meters	Cubic feet	35.314667
Cubic meters	Gallons (US liquid)	264.17205
Cubic meters	Quarts (US liquid)	1,056.6882
Cubic yards	Cubic centimeters	764,554.86
Cubic yards	Cubic feet	27
Cubic yards	Cubic inches	46,656
Cubic yards	Liters	764,554.86
Cubic yards	Quarts (US liquid)	807.89610
Days (mean solar)	Days (sidereal)	1.0027379
Days (mean solar)	Hours (mean solar)	24
Days (mean solar)	Hours (sidereal)	24.065710
Days (mean solar)	Years (calendar)	0.002739726
Days (mean solar)	Years (sidereal)	0.0027378031
Days (mean solar)	Years (tropical)	0.0027379093
Days (sidereal)	Days (mean solar)	0.99726957
Days (sidereal)	Hours (mean solar)	23.93447
Days (sidereal)	Hours (sidereal)	24
Days (sidereal)	Minutes (mean solar)	1,436.0682

(continued)

10. Units: Conversions and Constants *(continued)*

From	To	× **By**
Days (sidereal)	Minutes (sidereal)	1,440
Days (sidereal)	Seconds (sidereal)	86,400
Days (sidereal)	Years (calendar)	0.0027322454
Days (sidereal)	Years (sidereal)	0.0027303277
Days (sidereal)	Years (tropical)	0.0027304336
Decibels	Bels	0.1
Decimeters	Feet	0.32808399
Decimeters	Inches	3.9370079
Decimeters	Meters	0.1
Degrees	Minutes	60
Degrees	Radians	0.017453293
Degrees	Seconds	3,600
Degrees	Circles	0.0027777
Degrees	Quadrants	0.0111111
Dekaliters	Pecks (US)	1.135136
Dekaliters	Pints (US dry)	19.16217
Dekameters	Feet	32.808399
Dekameters	Inches	393.70079
Dekameters	Yards	10.93613
Dekameters	Centimeters	1,000
Fathoms	Centimeters	182.88
Fathoms	Feet	6
Fathoms	Inches	72
Fathoms	Meters	1.8288
Fathoms	Miles (nautical International)	0.00098747300
Fathoms	Miles (statute)	0.001136363
Fathoms	Yards	2
Feet	Centimeters	30.48
Feet	Fathoms	0.166666
Feet	Furlongs	0.00151515
Feet	Inches	12
Feet	Meters	0.3048
Feet	Microns	304800
Feet	Miles (nautical International)	0.00016457883
Feet	Miles (statute)	0.000189393
Feet	Rods	0.060606
Feet	Yards	0.333333
Gallons (US liquid)	Acre-feet	3.0688833×10^{-6}
Gallons (US liquid)	Barrels (US liquid)	0.031746032

(continued)

10. Units: Conversions and Constants *(continued)*

From	To	× By
Gallons (US liquid)	Bushels (US)	0.10742088
Gallons (US liquid)	Cubic centimeters	3,785.4118
Gallons (US liquid)	Cubic feet	0.133680555
Gallons (US liquid)	Cubic inches	231
Gallons (US liquid)	Cubic meters	0.0037854118
Gallons (US liquid)	Cubic yards	0.0049511317
Gallons (US liquid)	Gallons (US dry)	0.85936701
Gallons (US liquid)	Gallons (wine)	1
Gallons (US liquid)	Gills (US)	32
Gallons (US liquid)	Liters	3.7854118
Gallons (US liquid)	Ounces (US fluid)	128
Gallons (US liquid)	Pints (US liquid)	8
Gallons (US liquid)	Quarts (US liquid)	4
Grains	Carats (metric)	0.32399455
Grains	Drams (apoth. or troy)	0.016666
Grains	Drams (avdp.)	0.036671429
Grains	Grams	0.06479891
Grains	Milligrams	64.79891
Grains	Ounces (apoth. or troy)	0.0020833
Grains	Ounces (avdp.)	0.0022857143
Grams	Carats (metric)	5
Grams	Drams (apoth. or troy)	0.25720597
Grams	Drams (avdp.)	0.56438339
Grams	Dynes	980.665
Grams	Grains	15.432358
Grams	Ounces (apoth. or troy)	0.032150737
Grams	Ounces (avdp.)	0.035273962
Gravitational constant	Centimeters/(second × second)	980.621
Gravitational constant = G	Dyne $cm^2\,g^{-2}$	$6.6732\,(31) \times 10^{-8}$
Gravitational constant	Feet/(second × second)	32.1725
Gravitational constant = G	N $m^2\,kg^{-2}$	$6.6732\,(31) \times 10^{-11}$
Gravity on Earth = 1	Gravity on Jupiter	2.305
Gravity on Earth = 1	Gravity on Mars	0.3627 Equatorial
Gravity on Earth = 1	Gravity on Mercury	0.3648 Equatorial
Gravity on Earth = 1	Gravity on Moon	0.1652 Equatorial
Gravity on Earth = 1	Gravity on Neptune	1.323 ± 0.210 Equatorial
Gravity on Earth = 1	Gravity on Pluto	0.0225 ± 0.217 Equatorial
Gravity on Earth = 1	Gravity on Saturn	0.8800 Equatorial
Gravity on Earth = 1	Gravity on Sun	27.905 Equatorial

(continued)

*Easy Science Demos & Labs:
Earth Science*

10. Units: Conversions and Constants (continued)

From	To	× By
Gravity on Earth = 1	Gravity on Uranus	0.9554 ± 0.168 Equatorial
Gravity on Earth = 1	Gravity on Venus	0.9049 Equatorial
Hectares	Acres	2.4710538
Hectares	Square feet	107,639.10
Hectares	Square meters	10,000
Hectares	Square miles	0.0038610216
Hectares	Square rods	395.36861
Hectograms	Pounds (apoth. or troy)	0.26792289
Hectograms	Pounds (avdp.)	0.22046226
Hectoliters	Cubic centimeters	1.00028×10^5
Hectoliters	Cubic feet	3.531566
Hectoliters	Gallons (US liquid)	26.41794
Hectoliters	Ounces (US fluid)	3,381.497
Hectoliters	Pecks (US)	11.35136
Hectometers	Feet	328.08399
Hectometers	Rods	19.883878
Hectometers	Yards	109.3613
Horsepower	Horsepower (electric)	0.999598
Horsepower	Horsepower (metric)	1.01387
Horsepower	Kilowatts	0.745700
Horsepower	Kilowatts (International)	0.745577
Horsepower-hours	Kilowatts-hours	0.745700
Horsepower-hours	Watt-hours	745.700
Hours (mean solar)	Days (mean solar)	0.0416666
Hours (mean solar)	Days (sidereal)	0.041780746
Hours (mean solar)	Hours (sidereal)	1.00273791
Hours (mean solar)	Minutes (mean solar)	60
Hours (mean solar)	Minutes (sidereal)	60.164275
Hours (mean solar)	Seconds (mean solar)	3,600
Hours (mean solar)	Seconds (sidereal)	3,609.8565
Hours (mean solar)	Weeks (mean calendar)	0.0059523809
Hours (sidereal)	Days (mean solar)	0.41552899
Hours (sidereal)	Days (sidereal)	0.0416666
Hours (sidereal)	Hours (mean solar)	0.99726957
Hours (sidereal)	Minutes (mean solar)	59.836174
Hours (sidereal)	Minutes (sidereal)	60
Inches	Ångström units	2.54×10^8
Inches	Centimeters	2.54
Inches	Cubits	0.055555

(continued)

© 1997, 2003
J. Weston Walch, Publisher

Easy Science Demos & Labs:
Earth Science

10. Units: Conversions and Constants (continued)

From	To	× By
Inches	Fathoms	0.013888
Inches	Feet	0.083333
Inches	Meters	0.0254
Inches	Mils	1,000
Inches	Yards	0.027777
Kilograms	Drams (apoth. or troy)	257.20597
Kilograms	Drams (avdp.)	564.38339
Kilograms	Dynes	980,665
Kilograms	Grains	15,432.358
Kilograms	Hundredweights (long)	0.019684131
Kilograms	Hundredweights (short)	0.022046226
Kilograms	Ounces (apoth. or troy)	32.150737
Kilograms	Ounces (avdp.)	35.273962
Kilograms	Pennyweights	643.01493
Kilograms	Pounds (apoth. or troy)	2.6792289
Kilograms	Pounds (avdp.)	2.2046226
Kilograms	Quarters (US long)	0.0039368261
Kilograms	Scruples (apoth.)	771.61792
Kilograms	Tons (long)	0.00098420653
Kilograms	Tons (metric)	0.001
Kilograms	Tons (short)	0.0011023113
Kilograms/cubic meter	Grams/cubic centimeter	0.001
Kilograms/cubic meter	Pounds/cubic foot	0.062427961
Kilograms/cubic meter	Pounds/cubic inch	3.6127292×10^{-5}
Kiloliters	Cubic centimeters	1×10^{6}
Kiloliters	Cubic feet	35.31566
Kiloliters	Cubic inches	61,025.45
Kiloliters	Cubic meters	1.000028
Kiloliters	Cubic yards	1.307987
Kiloliters	Gallons (US dry)	27.0271
Kiloliters	Gallons (US liquid)	264.1794
Kilometers	Astronomical units	6.68878×10^{-9}
Kilometers	Feet	3,280.8399
Kilometers	Light-years	1.05702×10^{-13}
Kilometers	Miles (nautical International)	0.53995680
Kilometers	Miles (statute)	0.62137119
Kilometers	Rods	198.83878
Kilometers	Yards	1,093.6133
Kilometers/hour	Centimeters/second	27.7777

(continued)

10. Units: Conversions and Constants *(continued)*

From	To	× By
Kilometers/hour	Feet/hour	3,280.8399
Kilometers/hour	Feet/minute	54.680665
Kilometers/hour	Knots (International)	0.53995680
Kilometers/hour	Meters/second	0.277777
Kilometers/hour	Miles (statute)/hour	0.62137119
Kilometers/minute	Centimeters/second	1,666.666
Kilometers/minute	Feet/minute	3,280.8399
Kilometers/minute	Kilometers/hour	60
Kilometers/minute	Knots (International)	32.397408
Kilometers/minute	Miles/hour	37.282272
Kilometers/minute	Miles/minute	0.62137119
Kilowatt-hours	Joules	3.6×10^6
Light, velocity of	Kilometers/second ± 1.1	299,792.4562 (meters/second 100 × more accurate)
Light, velocity of	Meters/second ± 0.33 ppm	2.9979250×10^8
Light, velocity of	Centimeters/second ± 0.33 ppm	2.9979250×10^{10}
Light-years	Astronomical units	63,279.5
Light-years	Kilometers	9.46055×10^{12}
Light-years	Miles (statute)	5.87851×10^{12}
Liters	Bushels (US)	0.02837839
Liters	Cubic centimeters	1,000
Liters	Cubic feet	0.03531566
Liters	Cubic inches	61.02545
Liters	Cubic meters	0.001
Liters	Cubic yards	0.001307987
Liters	Drams (US fluid)	270.5198
Liters	Gallons (US dry)	0.2270271
Liters	Gallons (US liquid)	0.2641794
Liters	Gills (US)	8.453742
Liters	Hogsheads	0.004193325
Liters	Minims (US)	16,231.19
Liters	Ounces (US fluid)	33.81497
Liters	Pecks (US)	0.1135136
Liters	Pints (US dry)	1.816217
Liters	Pints (US liquid)	2.113436
Liters	Quarts (US dry)	0.9081084
Liters	Quarts (US liquid)	1.056718
Liters/minute	Cubic feet/minute	0.03531566
Liters/minute	Cubic feet/second	0.0005885943

(continued)

10. Units: Conversions and Constants (continued)

From	To	× By
Liters/minute	Gallons (US liquid)/minute	0.2641794
Liters/second	Cubic feet/minute	2.118939
Liters/second	Cubic feet/second	0.03531566
Liters/second	Cubic yards/minute	0.07847923
Liters/second	Gallons (US liquid)/minute	15.85077
Liters/second	Gallons (US liquid)/second	0.2641794
Lumens	Candle power	0.079577472
Meters	Ångström units	1×10^{10}
Meters	Fathoms	0.54680665
Meters	Feet	3.2808399
Meters	Furlongs	0.0049709695
Meters	Inches	39.370079
Meters	Megameters	1×10^{-6}
Meters	Miles (nautical International)	0.00053995680
Meters	Miles (statute)	0.00062137119
Meters	Millimicrons	1×10^{9}
Meters	Mils	39,370.079
Meters	Rods	0.19883878
Meters	Yards	1.0936133
Meters/hour	Feet/hour	3.2808399
Meters/hour	Feet/minute	0.054680665
Meters/hour	Knots (International)	0.00053995680
Meters/hour	Miles (statute)/hour	0.00062137119
Meters/minute	Centimeters/second	1.666666
Meters/minute	Feet/minute	3.2808399
Meters/minute	Feet/second	0.054680665
Meters/minute	Kilometers/hour	0.06
Meters/minute	Knots (International)	0.032397408
Meters/minute	Miles (statute)/hour	0.037282272
Meters/second	Feet/minute	196.85039
Meters/second	Feet/second	3.2808399
Meters/second	Kilometers/hour	3.6
Meters/second	Kilometers/minute	0.06
Meters/second	Miles (statute)/hour	2.2369363
Meter-candles	Lumens/square meter	1
Micrograms	Grams	1×10^{-6}
Micrograms	Milligrams	0.001
Micromicrons	Ångström units	0.01
Micromicrons	Centimeters	1×10^{-10}

(continued)

Easy Science Demos & Labs:
Earth Science

10. Units: Conversions and Constants *(continued)*

From	To	× By
Micromicrons	Inches	$3.9370079 \times 10^{-11}$
Micromicrons	Meters	1×10^{-12}
Micromicrons	Microns	1×10^{-6}
Microns	Ångström units	10,000
Microns	Centimeters	0.0001
Microns	Feet	3.2808399×10^{-6}
Microns	Inches	3.9370070×10^{-5}
Microns	Meters	1×10^{-6}
Microns	Millimeters	0.001
Microns	Millimicrons	1,000
Miles (statute)	Centimeters	160,934.4
Miles (statute)	Feet	5,280
Miles (statute)	Furlongs	8
Miles (statute)	Inches	63,360
Miles (statute)	Kilometers	1.609344
Miles (statute)	Light-years	1.70111×10^{-13}
Miles (statute)	Meters	1,600.344
Miles (statute)	Miles (nautical International)	0.86897624
Miles (statute)	Myriameters	0.1609344
Miles (statute)	Rods	320
Miles (statute)	Yards	1,760
Miles/hour	Centimeters/second	44.704
Miles/hour	Feet/hour	5,280
Miles/hour	Feet/minute	88
Miles/hour	Feet/second	1.466666
Miles/hour	Kilometers/hour	1.609344
Miles/hour	Knots (International)	0.86897624
Miles/hour	Meters/minute	26.8224
Miles/hour	Miles/minute	0.0166666
Miles/minute	Centimeters/second	2,682.24
Miles/minute	Feet/hour	316,800
Miles/minute	Feet/second	88
Miles/minute	Kilometers/minute	1.609344
Miles/minute	Knots (International)	52.138574
Miles/minute	Meters/minute	1,609.344
Miles/minute	Miles/hour	60
Milligrams	Carats (1877)	0.004871
Milligrams	Carats (metric)	0.005
Milligrams	Drams (apoth. or troy)	0.00025720597

(continued)

Easy Science Demos & Labs:
Earth Science

From	To	× By
Milligrams	Drams (advp.)	0.00056438339
Milligrams	Grains	0.015432358
Milligrams	Grams	0.001
Milligrams	Ounces (apoth. or troy)	3.2150737×10^{-5}
Milligrams	Ounces (avdp.)	3.5273962×10^{-5}
Milligrams	Pounds (apoth. or troy)	2.6792289×10^{-6}
Milligrams	Pounds (avdp.)	2.2046226×10^{-6}
Milligrams/liter	Grains/gallon (US)	0.05841620
Milligrams/liter	Grams/liter	0.001
Milligrams/liter	Parts/million	1; solvent density = 1
Milligrams/liter	Pounds/cubic foot	6.242621×10^{-5}
Milligrams/millimeter	Dynes/centimeter	9.80665
Milliliters	Cubic centimeters	1
Milliliters	Cubic inches	0.06102545
Milliliters	Drams (US fluid)	0.2705198
Milliliters	Gills (US)	0.008453742
Milliliters	Minims (US)	16.23119
Milliliters	Ounces (US fluid)	0.03381497
Milliliters	Pints (US liquid)	0.002113436
Millimeters	Ångström units	1×10^{7}
Millimeters	Centimeters	0.1
Millimeters	Decimeters	0.01
Millimeters	Dekameters	0.0001
Millimeters	Feet	0.0032808399
Millimeters	Inches	0.039370079
Millimeters	Meters	0.001
Millimeters	Microns	1,000
Millimeters	Mils	39.370079
Millimicrons	Ångström units	10
Millimicrons	Centimeters	1×10^{-7}
Millimicrons	Inches	3.9370079×10^{-8}
Millimicrons	Microns	0.001
Millimicrons	Millimeters	1×10^{-6}
Minutes (angular)	Degrees	0.0166666
Minutes (angular)	Quadrants	0.000185185
Minutes (angular)	Radians	0.00029088821
Minutes (angular)	Seconds (angular)	60
Minutes (mean solar)	Days (mean solar)	0.0006944444
Minutes (mean solar)	Days (sidereal)	0.00069634577

(continued)

From	To	× By
Minutes (mean solar)	Hours (mean solar)	0.0166666
Minutes (mean solar)	Hours (sidereal)	0.016732298
Minutes (mean solar)	Minutes (sidereal)	1.00273791
Minutes (sidereal)	Days (mean solar)	0.00069254831
Minutes (sidereal)	Minutes (mean solar)	0.99726957
Minutes (sidereal)	Months (mean calendar)	2.2768712×10^{-5}
Minutes (sidereal)	Seconds (sidereal)	60
Minutes/centimeter	Radians/centimeter	0.00029088821
Months (lunar)	Days (mean solar)	29.530588
Months (lunar)	Hours (mean solar)	708.73411
Months (lunar)	Minutes (mean solar)	42,524.047
Months (lunar)	Seconds (mean solar)	2.5514428×10^{-5}
Months (lunar)	Weeks (mean calendar)	4.2186554
Months (mean calendar)	Days (mean solar)	30.416666
Months (mean calendar)	Hours (mean solar)	730
Months (mean calendar)	Months (lunar)	1.0300055
Months (mean calendar)	Weeks (mean calendar)	4.3452381
Months (mean calendar)	Years (calendar)	0.08333333
Months (mean calendar)	Years (sidereal)	0.083274845
Months (mean calendar)	Years (tropical)	0.083278075
Myriagrams	Pounds (avdp.)	22.046226
Ounces (avdp.)	Drams (apoth. or troy)	7.291666
Ounces (avdp.)	Drams (avdp.)	16
Ounces (avdp.)	Grains	437.5
Ounces (avdp.)	Grams	28.349
Ounces (avdp.)	Ounces (apoth. or troy)	0.9114583
Ounces (avdp.)	Pounds (apoth. or troy)	0.075954861
Ounces (avdp.)	Pounds (avdp.)	0.0625
Ounces (US fluid)	Cubic centimeters	29.573730
Ounces (US fluid)	Cubic inches	1.8046875
Ounces (US fluid)	Cubic meters	2.9573730×10^{-5}
Ounces (US fluid)	Drams (US fluid)	8
Ounces (US fluid)	Gallons (US dry)	0.0067138047
Ounces (US fluid)	Gallons (US liquid)	0.0078125
Ounces (US fluid)	Gills (US)	0.25
Ounces (US fluid)	Liters	0.029572702
Ounces (US fluid)	Pints (US liquid)	0.0625
Ounces (US fluid)	Quarts (US liquid)	0.03125
Ounces/square inch	Dynes/square centimeter	4309.22

(continued)

10. Units: Conversions and Constants *(continued)*

From	To	× **By**
Ounces/square inch	Grams/square centimeter	4.3941849
Ounces/square inch	Pounds/square foot	9
Ounces/square inch	Pounds/square inch	0.0625
Parts/million	Grains/gallon (US)	0.05841620
Parts/million	Grams/liter	0.001
Parts/million	Milligrams/liter	1
Pints (US dry)	Bushels (US)	0.015625
Pints (US dry)	Cubic centimeters	550.61047
Pints (US dry)	Cubic inches	33.6003125
Pints (US dry)	Gallons (US dry)	0.125
Pints (US dry)	Gallons (US liquid)	0.14545590
Pints (US dry)	Liters	0.5505951
Pints (US dry)	Pecks (US)	0.0625
Pints (US dry)	Quarts (US dry)	0.5
Pints (US liquid)	Cubic centimeters	473.17647
Pints (US liquid)	Cubic feet	0.016710069
Pints (US liquid)	Cubic inches	28.875
Pints (US liquid)	Cubic yards	0.00061889146
Pints (US liquid)	Drama (US fluid)	128
Pints (US liquid)	Gallons (US liquid)	0.125
Pints (US liquid)	Gills (US)	4
Pints (US liquid)	Liters	0.4731632
Pints (US liquid)	Milliliters	473.1632
Pints (US liquid)	Minims (US)	7,680
Pints (US liquid)	Ounces (US fluid)	16
Pints (US liquid)	Quarts (US liquid)	0.5
Planck's constant	Erg-seconds	6.6255×10^{-27}
Planck's constant	Joule-seconds	6.6255×10^{-34}
Planck's constant	Joule-seconds/Avog. No. (chem.)	3.9905×10^{-10}
Pounds (apoth. or troy)	Drams (apoth. or troy)	96
Pounds (apoth. or troy)	Drams (avdp.)	210.65143
Pounds (apoth. or troy)	Grains	5,780
Pounds (apoth. or troy)	Grams	373.24172
Pounds (apoth. or troy)	Kilograms	0.37324172
Pounds (apoth. or troy)	Ounces (apoth. or troy)	12
Pounds (apoth. or troy)	Ounces (avdp.)	13.165714
Pounds (apoth. or troy)	Pounds (avdp.)	0.8228571
Pounds (avdp.)	Drams (apoth. or troy)	116.6686
Pounds (avdp.)	Drams (avdp.)	256

(continued)

From	To	× By
Pounds (avdp.)	Grains	7,000
Pounds (avdp.)	Grams	453.59237
Pounds (avdp.)	Kilograms	0.45359237
Pounds (avdp.)	Ounces (apoth. or troy)	14.593333
Pounds (avdp.)	Ounces (avdp.)	16
Pounds (avdp.)	Pounds (apoth. or troy)	1.215277
Pounds (avdp.)	Scruples (apoth.)	350
Pounds (avdp.)	Tons (long)	0.00044642857
Pounds (avdp.)	Tons (metric)	0.00045359237
Pounds (avdp.)	Tons (short)	0.0005
Pounds/cubic foot	Grams/cubic centimeter	0.016018463
Pounds/cubic foot	Kilograms/cubic meter	16.018463
Pounds/cubic inch	Grams/cubic centimeter	27.679905
Pounds/cubic inch	Grams/liter	27.68068
Pounds/cubic inch	Kilograms/cubic meter	27,679.005
Pounds/gallon (US liquid)	Grams/cubic centimeter	0.11982643
Pounds/gallon (US liquid)	Pounds/cubic foot	7.4805195
Pounds/inch	Grams/centimeter	178.57967
Pounds/inch	Grams/foot	5,443.1084
Pounds/inch	Grams/inch	453.59237
Pounds/inch	Ounces/centimeter	6.2992
Pounds/inch	Ounces/inch	16
Pounds/inch	Pounds/meter	39.370079
Pounds/minute	Kilograms/hour	27.2155422
Pounds/minute	Kilograms/minute	0.45359237
Pounds on Earth = 1	Pounds on Jupiter	2.529 Equatorial
Pounds on Earth = 1	Pounds on Mars	0.3627 Equatorial
Pounds on Earth = 1	Pounds on Mercury	0.3648 Equatorial
Pounds on Earth = 1	Pounds on Moon	0.1652 Equatorial
Pounds on Earth = 1	Pounds on Neptune	1.323 ± 0.210 Equatorial
Pounds on Earth = 1	Pounds on Pluto	0.0225 ± 0.217 Equatorial
Pounds on Earth = 1	Pounds on Saturn	0.8800 Equatorial
Pounds on Earth = 1	Pounds on Sun	27.905 Equatorial
Pounds on Earth = 1	Pounds on Uranus	0.9554 ± 0.168 Equatorial
Pounds on Earth = 1	Pounds on Venus	0.9049 Equatorial
Pounds/square foot	Atmospheres	0.000472541
Pounds/square foot	Bars	0.000478803
Pounds/square foot	Centimeter of Hg (0°C)	0.0359131
Pounds/square foot	Dynes/square centimeter	478.803

(continued)

10. Units: Conversions and Constants *(continued)*

From	To	× By
Pounds/square foot	Feet of air (1 atm. 60°F)	13.096
Pounds/square foot	Grams/square centimeter	0.48824276
Pounds/square foot	Kilograms/square meter	4.8824276
Pounds/square foot	Millimeters of Hg (0°C)	0.369131
Pounds/square inch	Atmospheres	0.0680460
Pounds/square inch	Bars	0.0689476
Pounds/square inch	Dynes/square centimeter	68,947.6
Pounds/square inch	Grams/square centimeter	70.306958
Pounds/square inch	Kilograms/square centimeter	0.070306958
Pounds/square inch	Millimeters of Hg (0°C)	51.7149
Quarts (US dry)	Bushels (US)	0.03125
Quarts (US dry)	Cubic centimeters	1,101.2209
Quarts (US dry)	Cubic feet	0.038889251
Quarts (US dry)	Cubic inches	67.200625
Quarts (US dry)	Gallons (US dry)	0.25
Quarts (US dry)	Gallons (US liquid)	0.29091180
Quarts (US dry)	Liters	1.1011901
Quarts (US dry)	Pecks (US)	0.125
Quarts (US dry)	Pints (US dry)	2
Quarts (US liquid)	Cubic centimeters	946.35295
Quarts (US liquid)	Cubic feet	0.033420136
Quarts (US liquid)	Cubic inches	57.75
Quarts (US liquid)	Drams (US fluid)	256
Quarts (US liquid)	Gallons (US dry)	0.21484175
Quarts (US liquid)	Gallons (US liquid)	0.25
Quarts (US liquid)	Gills (US)	8
Quarts (US liquid)	Liters	0.9463264
Quarts (US liquid)	Ounces (US fluid)	32
Quarts (US liquid)	Pints (US liquid)	2
Quarts (US liquid)	Quarts (US dry)	0.8593670
Quintals (metric)	Grams	100,000
Quintals (metric)	Hundredweights (long)	1.9684131
Quintals (metric)	Kilograms	100
Quintals (metric)	Pounds (avdp.)	220.46226
Radians	Circumferences	0.15915494
Radians	Degrees	57.295779
Radians	Minutes	3,437.7468
Radians	Quadrants	0.63661977
Radians	Revolutions	0.15915494

(continued)

© 1997, 2003
J. Weston Walch, Publisher

*Easy Science Demos & Labs:
Earth Science*

From	To	× **By**
Revolutions	Degrees	360
Revolutions	Grades	400
Revolutions	Quadrants	4
Revolutions	Radians	6.2831853
Seconds (angular)	Degrees	0.000277777
Seconds (angular)	Minutes	0.0166666
Seconds (angular)	Radians	4.8481368×10^{-6}
Seconds (mean solar)	Days (mean solar)	1.1574074×10^{-5}
Seconds (mean solar)	Days (sidereal)	1.1605763×10^{-5}
Seconds (mean solar)	Hours (mean solar)	0.0002777777
Seconds (mean solar)	Hours (sidereal)	0.00027853831
Seconds (mean solar)	Minutes (mean solar)	0.0166666
Seconds (mean solar)	Minutes (sidereal)	0.016712298
Seconds (mean solar)	Seconds (sidereal)	1.00273791
Seconds (sidereal)	Days (mean solar)	1.1542472×10^{-5}
Seconds (sidereal)	Days (sidereal)	1.1574074×10^{-5}
Seconds (sidereal)	Hours (mean solar)	0.00027701932
Seconds (sidereal)	Hours (sidereal)	0.000277777
Seconds (sidereal)	Minutes (mean solar)	0.016621159
Seconds (sidereal)	Minutes (sidereal)	0.0166666
Seconds (sidereal)	Seconds (mean solar)	0.09726957
Square centimeters	Square decimeters	0.01
Square centimeters	Square feet	0.0010763910
Square centimeters	Square inches	0.15500031
Square centimeters	Square meters	0.0001
Square centimeters	Square millimeters	100
Square centimeters	Square miles	1.5500031×10^{5}
Square centimeters	Square yards	0.00011959900
Square decimeters	Square centimeters	100
Square decimeters	Square inches	15.500031
Square dekameters	Acres	0.024710538
Square dekameters	Ares	1
Square dekameters	Square meters	100
Square dekameters	Square yards	119.59900
Square feet	Acres	2.295684×10^{-5}
Square feet	Ares	0.0009290304
Square feet	Square centimeters	929.0304
Square feet	Square inches	144
Square feet	Square meters	0.09290304

(continued)

10. Units: Conversions and Constants *(continued)*

From	To	× **By**
Square feet	Square miles	3.5870064×10^{-8}
Square feet	Square yards	0.111111
Square hectometers	Square meters	10,000
Square inches	Square centimeters	6.4516
Square inches	Square decimeters	0.064516
Square inches	Square feet	0.0069444
Square inches	Square meters	0.00064516
Square inches	Square miles	$2.4909767 \times 10^{-10}$
Square inches	Square millimeters	645.16
Square inches	Square mils	1×10^{-6}
Square kilometers	Acres	247.10538
Square kilometers	Square feet	1.0763010×10^{7}
Square kilometers	Square inches	1.5500031×10^{9}
Square kilometers	Square meters	1×10^{6}
Square kilometers	Square miles	0.38610216
Square kilometers	Square yards	1.1959900×10^{6}
Square meters	Acres	0.00024710538
Square meters	Ares	0.01
Square meters	Hectares	0.0001
Square meters	Square centimeters	10,000
Square meters	Square feet	10.763910
Square meters	Square inches	1,550.0031
Square meters	Square kilometers	1×10^{-6}
Square meters	Square miles	3.8610218×10^{-7}
Square meters	Square millimeters	1×10^{6}
Square meters	Square yards	1.1959900
Square miles	Acres	640
Square miles	Hectares	258.99881
Square miles	Square feet	2.7878288×10^{7}
Square miles	Square kilometers	2.5899881
Square miles	Square meters	2.5899881×10^{6}
Square miles	Square rods	102,400
Square miles	Square yards	3.0976×10^{6}
Square millimeters	Square centimeters	0.01
Square millimeters	Square inches	0.0015500031
Square millimeters	Square meters	1×10^{-6}
Square yards	Acres	0.00020661157
Square yards	Ares	0.0083612736
Square yards	Hectares	8.3612736×10^{-5}

(continued)

10. Units: Conversions and Constants (continued)

From	To	× By
Square yards	Square centimeters	8,361.2736
Square yards	Square feet	9
Square yards	Square inches	1,296
Square yards	Square meters	0.83612736
Square yards	Square miles	$3.228305785 \times 10^{-7}$
Tons (long)	Kilograms	1,016.0469
Tons (long)	Ounces (avdp.)	35,840
Tons (long)	Pounds (apoth. or troy)	2,722.22
Tons (long)	Pounds (avdp.)	2,240
Tons (long)	Tons (metric)	1.0160469
Tons (long)	Tons (short)	1.12
Tons (metric)	Dynes	9.80665×10^8
Tons (metric)	Grams	1×10^6
Tons (metric)	Kilograms	1,000
Tons (metric)	Ounces (avdp.)	35,273.962
Tons (metric)	Pounds (apoth. or troy)	2,679.2289
Tons (metric)	Pounds (avdp.)	2,204.6226
Tons (metric)	Tons (long)	0.98420653
Tons (metric)	Tons (short)	1.1023113
Tons (short)	Kilograms	907.18474
Tons (short)	Ounces (avdp.)	32,000
Tons (short)	Pounds (apoth. or troy)	2,430.555
Tons (short)	Pounds (avdp.)	2,000
Tons (short)	Tons (long)	0.89285714
Tons (short)	Tons (metric)	0.90718474
Velocity of light	Centimeters/second ± 0.33 ppm	$2.9979250\,(10) \times 10^{10}$
Velocity of light	Meters/second ± 0.33 ppm	$2.9979250\,(10) \times 10^8$
Velocity of light (100 x more accurate)	Kilometers/second ± 1.1 meter/second	2.997924562×10^5
Volts	Mks. (r or nr) units	1
Volts (International)	Volts	1.000330
Volts-seconds	Maxwells	1×10^8
Watts	Kilowatts	0.001
Watts (International)	Watts	1.000165
Weeks (mean calendar)	Days (mean solar)	7
Weeks (mean calendar)	Days (sidereal)	7.0191654
Weeks (mean calendar)	Hours (mean solar)	168
Weeks (mean calendar)	Hours (sidereal)	168.45997
Weeks (mean calendar)	Minutes (mean solar)	10,080

(continued)

10. Units: Conversions and Constants *(continued)*

From	To	× **By**
Weeks (mean calendar)	Minutes (sidereal)	10,107.598
Weeks (mean calendar)	Months (lunar)	0.23704235
Weeks (mean calendar)	Months (mean calendar)	0.23013699
Weeks (mean calendar)	Years (calendar)	0.019178082
Weeks (mean calendar)	Years (sidereal)	0.019164622
Weeks (mean calendar)	Years (tropical)	0.019165365
Yards	Centimeters	91.44
Yards	Cubits	2
Yards	Fathoms	0.5
Yards	Feet	3
Yards	Furlongs	0.00454545
Yards	Inches	36
Yards	Meters	0.9144
Yards	Rods	0.181818
Yards	Spans	4
Years (calendar)	Days (mean solar)	365
Years (calendar)	Hours (mean solar)	8,760
Years (calendar)	Minutes (mean solar)	525,600
Years (calendar)	Months (lunar)	12.360065
Years (calendar)	Months (mean calendar)	12
Years (calendar)	Seconds (mean solar)	3.1536×10^7
Years (calendar)	Weeks (mean calendar)	52.142857
Years (calendar)	Years (sidereal)	0.99929814
Years (calendar)	Years (tropical)	0.99933690
Years (leap)	Days (mean solar)	366
Years (sidereal)	Days (mean solar)	365.25636
Years (sidereal)	Days (sidereal)	366.25640
Years (sidereal)	Years (calendar)	1.0007024
Years (sidereal)	Years (tropical)	1.0000388
Years (tropical)	Days (mean solar)	365.24219
Years (tropical)	Days (sidereal)	366.24219
Years (tropical)	Hours (mean solar)	8,765.8126
Years (tropical)	Hours (sidereal)	8,789.8126
Years (tropical)	Months (mean calendar)	12.007963
Years (tropical)	Seconds (mean solar)	3.1556926×10^7
Years (tropical)	Seconds (sidereal)	3.1643326×10^7
Years (tropical)	Weeks (mean calendar)	52.177456
Years (tropical)	Years (calendar)	1.0006635
Years (tropical)	Years (sidereal)	0.99996121

Easy Science Demos & Labs:
Earth Science

Glossary

A

absolute humidity: the actual amount of water vapor present in the air

acid rain: rain having increased acidity due to environmental pollutants

alluvial: pertaining to erosion byproducts, such as sediment deposited by flowing water

altitude: in astronomy, the distance above the horizon of some celestial body, measured in degrees

aneroid barometer: an instrument that detects variations in atmospheric pressure by bending a metallic surface, which moves a pointer

aphelion: the point in a planet's orbit that is farthest from the sun

apparent magnitude: the relative brightness of a celestial body indicated on a numerical scale

apparent temperature: the actual temperature adjusted for relative humidity; also called the comfort index or heat index

aquifer: a water-bearing layer of rock, sand, or gravel

astrolabe: a device for measuring astronomical altitude

astronomical unit (AU): a unit of length equal to the mean distance of Earth to the sun, or about 93 million miles (150 million kilometers)

atmosphere: thin layer of gases— including nitrogen, oxygen, ozone, and carbon—that surrounds Earth

B

brackish: water that is neither completely fresh nor completely saline

C

calcite: crystal form of calcium carbonite; component of chalk, limestone, and marble

chemical weathering: the action of airborne acids that damages living and nonliving things near Earth's surface

condensation: the process by which liquid is removed from a vapor

condensation nuclei: particles of dust, smoke, or other substances that form the centers of drops of water

conduction: transmission of electricity or heat through a medium

convection: heat transfer resulting from the movement of warmer substances upwards

coquina: soft limestone formed of broken shells and corals

crater: an indentation left in the ground after a high-velocity impact, such as a meteor striking Earth

crust: the rocky outer surface of Earth

crystals: the shapes into which nonliving substances, such as salt and ice, form

D

delta: a portion of a river named for its triangular shape, usually where the river joins the ocean

dew point: the temperature at which air becomes saturated and produces dew

(continued)

diffraction: the spreading out of waves, such as light waves, as they pass by the edge of an obstacle or through an opening

diffraction grating: a glass or plastic plate with parallel grooves or slits; produces optical spectra when white light strikes it

E

equinox: one of two days in Earth's year when the sun appears to be directly overhead at noon; on an equinox, the day and night have equal length.

erosion: the wearing away of soil and rock caused by the action of air, water, and temperature changes

evaporation: the changing of liquid into vapor

F

feldspar: mineral occuring in igneous and other rocks; one of the hardest minerals

fossil: imprint or remains of a plant or an animal from a past geological age

fossil fuel: burnable source of energy, such as coal, that is derived from compressed living matter that has changed chemically over millions of years

freefall: the condition of unrestrained motion in a gravitational field

G

gravity: the attraction between all objects because of their mass; the force that holds the universe together

groundwater: water underneath the earth's surface

H

halite: salt, or sodium chloride, in the form of solid masses; rock salt

headwater(s): a region where a river originates

hygrometer: an instrument that measures humidity in the air

I

igneous rock: rock formed by the cooling of melted material

inertia: the tendency of a motionless object to remain motionless or of a moving object to continue moving in the same direction unless disturbed by an outside force

infrared rays: beams of light lying slightly beyond the red end of the visible light spectrum; heat rays

inner core: the ball-shaped center of Earth, probably consisting of iron and nickel

isostasy: equilibrium resulting from equal pressure from all directions

L

latitude: the measurement of Earth away from its equator and toward its poles, measured in degrees

leeward: located in or facing the direction toward which the wind is blowing

light-year: the distance that light travels in a vacuum in one year—approximately 5,878 trillion miles

lodestone: a magnetized piece of the mineral form of black iron oxide

(continued)

longitude: the measurement of Earth away from an arbitrary point (Greenwich Mean), measured east and west in hours

M

mantle: thick layer of solid rock between the earth's crust and outer core

meander: in a river, a place where the speed of the water slows, characterized by twists and turns

meteor: chunk of space debris, usually made of iron and nickel

mirror telescope: telescope that uses a mirror rather than a lens to gather light; also called reflecting telescope

Mohs hardness scale: ten minerals from softest to hardest; the hardness of other minerals is determined by scratching them with minerals on the scale.

moraine: stones and debris carried along and deposited by a glacier; a ridge of debris on the surface of or at the edge of a glacier

O

outer core: layer of melted iron and nickel between Earth's mantle and inner core

oxbow: in a river, a region where two meandering banks join to form a pool

P

parallax: an apparent change in the position of an object, caused by a change in position from which the object is viewed

penumbra: a partial shadow between a perfect shadow and full light

perihelion: the point nearest the sun in a planet's orbit

photochemical: relating to the interactions of radiant energy and chemical systems

prism: a wedge-shaped transparent object used to disperse a beam of light, producing a spectrum

psychrometer: a device that uses the difference between the readings of two thermometers to measure humidity

R

radiation: the emission of radiant energy in the form of waves or particles

radioastronomy: the study of celestial objects by analyzing radio-frequency waves received from outside the earth's atmosphere

radiometer: an instrument that detects and measures radiation

refracting telescope: telescope that produces an enlarged image through the use of lenses

relative humidity: the amount of water vapor in the air compared to the maximum amount possible

revolution: the orbital motion of planets around the sun

rhyolite: glassy volcanic rock; the lava form of granite

rotation: the spinning motion of Earth and other planets around their axes

S

saturation: the point at which air at a specific temperature or soil is unable to hold more moisture; 100% relative humidity

(continued)

sediment: material that settles to the bottom of a liquid

sedimentary rock: rock formed from sediment transported by water

solstice: one of two days during which either day or night reaches its longest duration for the year

specific heat capacity: the amount of heat required to raise the temperature of a body one degree

spectroscopy: the study of spectra, bands of light

spectrum: a band of colors produced when light passes through a prism and spreads out; different light sources produce different spectra.

stalactite: rock formation hanging down from the roof of a cave, formed by the dripping of calcite-rich water

stalagmite: rock formation projecting upwards from the floor of a cave, formed by the dripping of calcite-rich water

streaking: scratching a mineral on a hard surface to examine the color of the powder as a means of identification

T

tectonic events: the motion of Earth's plates past each other, believed to cause most earthquakes, mountains, and volcanoes

tectonic plates: moving sections composing Earth's crust and upper mantle

thermal inversion: condition that occurs when a layer of stationary warm air settles over a layer of cool air, causing pollution to be trapped near the ground

thermochemical: relating to the interactions of thermal energy and chemical systems

thermocline: a layer that separates an upper, warmer zone of water from a lower, colder, heavier zone

thermohaline: involving temperature and salt content (salinity), a major cause of ocean current formation

touchstone: a stone used in ancient times to determine whether gold or silver was genuine

transpiration: the giving off of watery vapor through animal or plant pores

U

ultraviolet rays: beams of light located beyond the visible spectrum at its violet end

umbra: the darkest part of a shadow; part of a shadow that excludes all light

W

water table: the upper limit of the portion of the ground wholly saturated with water

wave trough: depression or lowest point between ocean waves or any waves

weathering: physical and chemical processes by which weather decomposes Earth's materials

windward: located in or facing the direction from which the wind blows

Z

zenith: the highest altitude at which a celestial body appears in the sky